CRY LOVE, CRY HOPE

CRY LOVE, CRY HOPE

—— Responding to AIDS ——

*

Edited by
BILL KIRKPATRICK

*

Foreword by
SHEILA CASSIDY

DARTON · LONGMAN + TODD

First published in 1994 by
Darton, Longman and Todd Ltd
1 Spencer Court
140–142 Wandsworth High Street
London SW18 4JJ

ISBN 0–232–52070–4

A catalogue record for this book is available
from the British Library

Cover: painting by Charalambos Sofianos; design by Bet Ayer

All royalties earned by the sale of this book
will be given to Reaching Out, a listening centre
for all those suffering from AIDS, their families and friends.

Phototypeset by Intype, London
Printed and bound in Great Britain
at the University Press, Cambridge

To Richie the inspirer,
whose life of caring
was towards the most
socially wounded in our society
and
to all carers, whatever
their label, in recognition that
in caring there is no 'them and us'

Contents

Foreword

I have read *Cry Love, Cry Hope* in two great gulps on the train between Oxford and Plymouth, and now, as we approach Exeter I search for words to communicate the experience. My first feelings were of mild irritation: the various short accounts by Richie McMullen's friends and carers of how they had known him seemed rather ordinary, hardly worth publishing. But then I told myself that of *course* they were ordinary, because Richie and Bill were, in some ways, an ordinary couple, plunged into the sadness of terminal illness. That's *one* way of looking at it. The other way to see it, of course, is that this book constitutes a collective act of enormous courage, because a group of professional people have dared to speak openly of their feelings.

No one who reads this book could dare to call gay love perverted: different it is, in some ways, but true love it is. Richie's poem, written for Bill (printed on the last pages), says it all:

> Love is straight,
> And love is gay.
> Love is great,
> And love, the way.

I think that what I find difficult about gay relationships is not the stable, long-term relationships but the short-term partnerships which seem to become physical at lightning speed. And yet, this is the way for so many heterosexual people too; there are more things in heaven and earth than I understand and I feel no competence to judge. In particular, I wonder why we never ask the question: what does it do to human beings to condemn their relationships sight unseen and thereby forcing them to live their lives in the shadows? Why do so many of us snigger at the idiosyncrasies of those we class as different while being quite blind to their gifts of tenderness and loyalty which are so often the *real* qualities that differentiate us. How would the heterosexual community cope with terrible long-drawn-out illnesses, the multiple tragic losses which have befallen the gay community? Surely we have much to learn from these, our brothers in Christ.

My hope is that this amazing and beautiful book will help many others, as it has helped me, along the path to non-judgementalism, to the great Christian gift of U.P.R., Carl Rogers' abbreviation for Unconditional Positive Regard, the stance which says, 'I will accept you as an individual person with the right to your own life, visions, and beliefs. Whatever you do, whatever you say, I will not reject you'. I think that Jesus was a Rogerian – or perhaps I should say that this aspect of Rogers' philosophy is profoundly Christian. 'Judge not that you may not be judged' is something we should write out a hundred times after each lapse into thinking ourselves holier than the next man or woman.

It occurs to me that the Richie McMullens, the David Randalls, the Bill Kirkpatricks of this world have been sent to remind us of the essentials of our Christian faith: that it is in washing each other's feet that we are most like the Master. If we allow ourselves to join the bystanders muttering at the promiscuity of the woman taken in adultery, we will, sure as eggs, find that it is our darkest and dirtiest secrets that are being written in the dust for all to see.

The other thing that strikes me is that this book is full of little nuggets of wisdom about pastoral care. David Randall's chapter in particular should be compulsory reading for hospital and hospice chaplains, as should Bill's painfully moving account of Richie's last days. I for one am profoundly grateful to Bill Kirkpatrick, not only for daring to allow his own personal call to love Richie McMullen as well as being an Anglican priest, but also for letting us share the agony of his letting go of a beloved friend and partner. My only sadness is that I never knew Richie, and my only complaint about this book is that it doesn't tell us more about a truly remarkable man.

Sheila Cassidy

Acknowledgements

Richie asked me to thank all the contributors for having the courage to be vulnerable in the sharing of their personal feelings as carers. He would be pleased to know that Betty Goodrum, an old friend and colleague from Centrepoint days, freely gave her time in typing and preparing the manuscript for publication.

Thanks to Jim Hall, who after reading the first draft said, 'This book is full of hope', giving the inspiration for the title *Cry Love, Cry Hope*.

Thanks to Fr David Randall for permission to use Charalambos Sofianos' painting, now hanging in the office of CARA, for the cover.

Thanks to Dr Sheila Cassidy for generously writing the foreword.

Many thanks not least of all to Mary Jean Pritchard, for encouragement, advice and sensitivity, as editor.

Finally, it is my hope that together we have all produced the kind of book that Richie envisaged and that carers and others will find encouraging.

Introduction

Richie McMullen inspired and initiated this book about two months before he died of opportunistic infections early on the morning of Friday 28 November 1991.

The idea for the book first came to him some months earlier. After a day which had been very long and tiring for me, Richie said, 'Bill, you look absolutely worn out. How do you cope with all this illness, all this dying you have been involved with for the past seven years?' So far as I can recall, my answer was along these lines: 'I am nurtured by the friendship of your loving me, by the family who have, and still are, supporting me in so many ways since Reaching Out came into being. I am supported by a spiritual companion and friend, by a very caring psychotherapist, by many others who surround this basic support group, and, of course, by the faith I attempt to live by'.

My reply to Richie's question reflected my experience that in caring for people with any lengthy, life-threatening illness, we become friends with the so-called 'patients'. In time, one loss is followed by many losses, with no time left for grieving in between. It is essential for us to express the feelings that arise from this and to have compassion for ourselves, as much as for others.

Richie believed that a book about such experiences of caring would be helpful for others in their care and support of persons living with HIV/AIDS. He felt especially that the book should be written by the different members of the care team, expressing their personal feelings and explaining how they cope with their emotions. He hoped that this would encourage others to know that it is all right – in fact essential – for carers to release those emotions, if they are

1

to remain alongside another person according to his or her needs, rather than their own.

Richie therefore asked several members of his own care team if they would contribute to such a book, and those who saw its value have done so. As one would expect, with articles coming from a broad spectrum of carers, the feelings they share vary considerably, but the general theme is that we are all in need of care and support. We are reminded that caring is a reciprocal action: there is no 'them and us'. It is through the truth of caring that we are drawn closer to each other in our common journey through life towards a wholeness that includes our dying.

Unfortunately, Richie's death prevented him from seeing many of the contributions and from editing the book as a whole. This has been left to me, assisted by Tony Masters.

Bill Kirkpatrick

Living with Empathetic Friends

Richie McMullen had a rich and varied life: handyman in his father's small business; rent boy; seaman; regular soldier; student nurse in a large mental hospital; volunteer youth worker in Liverpool, leading to his becoming a qualified youth and community worker in Liverpool and in London.

In 1972, he became a team leader with the Centrepoint project in Soho, setting up its first hostel. During this period, he also obtained his counselling diploma and began counselling men who had been sexually abused as youths, as he himself had been. In 1985, with Fr Bill, he co-founded Streetwise Youth, the first project in the UK to advise, support and counsel young men involved in prostitution at street level. In 1987, he co-founded, with Martin Dockerell, Survivors, a male rape support group, again the first of its kind in the UK.

In 1985 Richie was found to be HIV positive and was confirmed as having AIDS in 1987. Ironically, his illness became a very positive part of his life, as through it, he discovered his ability to write. His two-volume autobiography Enchanted Boy and Enchanted Youth (Gay Men's Press) was very well received by the press. He also published Living with HIV and Male Rape (Gay Men's Press); the latter was the first in-depth study of male rape to be published in this country.

Richie never remained silent on the sensitive issues relating to himself. His courage and compassion for others were expressed in his writings and in his campaigning for the gay community, for the abused and for the homeless. One of his main goals was to equate the law applying to male and female rape. A Private Member's Bill is currently being prepared to be presented to the House of Commons to this end. A recent BBC film, entitled 'Male Rape' includes a contribution from Richie and has recently been awarded a Howard League media award.

Richie's vulnerabilities were also his great strengths. He had the gift of being a communicator of warmth, with a fine sense of humour. He was extremely sensitive to the pain of others. He loved and supported me; he loved his home, his plants, his fish. He was a very private and yet public person. He was what I call a wounded healer. He was for me and for others a truly spiritual person. He believed that life was for loving and being loved. It was this factor that empowered his life and his healing to wholeness. On the tenth anniversary of our partnership he gave me the following outline of his expectations of the ideal friend/partner, stating that I had inspired it.

My empathetic friend sees the unique mystery that is me. Never fully understanding it nor too deeply exploring it, he allows it to be. He sees this mystery and knows it to be the evolving me. He sees and knows that it's mine and mine alone. He sees the possibilities for growth and allows it to happen. Sometimes the results please him, sometimes not. He sees the mystery that is me and lets it be, for me, for others and for himself. He sees me as a whole person. Not always complete and together, nor loose and lost. He sees the whole me and accepts this wholeness. This indeed makes him my friend. He sees the strengths and weaknesses, the potential and limitations, the clear views and the blockages, the caring and the selfishness, the harmony and the discord, the saint and the sinner. He sees it all and accepts. He sees the struggle and the ease of my move towards change and the greater me, and allows it to happen at my pace. He sometimes sees just how slow it is and how many backward steps I have to retrace in an effort to get it right in my own terms. He sees me as a person who knows the value of true friendship but also as a person who sometimes lets him down. He is safe in the knowledge that I

4

would never knowingly hurt him. So, when I do, the process of healing is co-creative. He knows that I'll try to dwell more on the recovery than on the hurt itself. He sees that, in wounding I'm wounded too. He sees the sensitivity that is in me and is careful to encourage and preserve it. But he also sees the times when I'm just a little too introspective and self-centred and he makes allowances. He sees the person who needs loving, who wants to give, who needs to be needed, the searcher after truth, the child and the adult, the poet and the writer, the Marxist who reads the Bible, the guy who says he wants a lot of new experiences but who is often just too lazy to move. My friend sees the paradox that is me and my efforts to work through it constructively. He sees the aggression and the frustration and my efforts to cope with such a powerful energy. He sees me growing through trying. He sees my HIV disease and does not make it the centre of his or my world. His seeing helps me see myself so much more honestly. The strength of his growing acceptance of the total me permits me to be growingly vulnerable towards him, so allowing myself to see myself as I am through his eyes. His 'seeing' and my acceptance of it allows the mystery that is me to remain intact and free to evolve.

Richie McMullen,
Living with HIV in Self and Others, Gay Men's Press,
1988, pp 68–9

If It Hadn't Been For You

Bill tells me that you would like me to contribute to an anthology of individual responses about AIDS. I would like to. I can write something now, at once, but I might want to alter it a bit later on or write it a bit better, as I can't quite get it together yet.

If it hadn't been for you, I don't think I would have come across AIDS very directly. It was because I had known you at Hatfield as your counselling tutor that it was so awful when you rang and said you were HIV positive. Yet it somehow seems that it is because of the virus that you have been able to be so creative – four books is an extraordinary achievement. You asked me to be on the management committee of Streetwise Youth; I was very moved by that and it has been one of the most upheaving experiences of my life. Somehow it has survived despite tremendous turmoil. Your dedication to the members has never been matched.

I'm terrified of illness; my father died suddenly of a virus over a period of a week when I was 3, and I've always been fearful. Somehow seeing you struggling with the virus and now dying helps lessen my fear. I also think of the people with the virus who work at Streetwise and who work so creatively with determination. I know someone who has haemophilia, and now HIV, who, as he says, was given riches which turned out to be poison. His struggle and rage has given him wisdom and stripped him to the basics.

It seems that those with AIDS have given me vision. I am not quite so frightened now.

Gillian

A Friend

'Will he see me, Sister?'
Standing in the corridor,
    heart pounding, mouth dry.
Desperately wanting to see you,
Desperately afraid.
'Oh, yes, he'll see you', she said
    and smiled into my eyes.

She opens the door, and I walk in,
Calm and confident and smiling.
I kiss you on your sunken cheek
    and take your hand in mine.
Disbelief turns into numbness,
I feel nothing, yet
    you must feel so much
Pain.
I talk of this and that,
and tell you of my plans and hopes and dreams
    and all the time, time is running out.

I long to say 'I love you'
    but you never liked that sort of thing.
You seemed to find it all so hard
    that someone else could ever love you.
Yet, you gave so much to others
    selflessly
    endlessly
I used to wonder would it never end
The well of Life
    never dying.

I've talked too much, you're tired.
I long to reach you, deep inside,
    but there it's private, private
    and so we talk of other things instead.

It's time to go, oh the hardest bit of all.
'Take care', I murmur, and give you one
    last kiss.
And outside I feel humbled,
    gratified and proud
To have loved someone who gave so much.

Maggie

AIDS: It Was Only A Word

AIDS: it was only a word to me. People told me about it. I read articles on it in the *Guardian* and felt a detached sorrow when I thought of the fear and, later, the pain AIDS victims had to endure. It was not something that had affected me personally; in our country community no one seemed to have AIDS.

Richie McMullen had been a friend years ago. I didn't know him very well and we had lost touch. Through a mutual friend, I heard he was HIV positive, but he had full-blown AIDS before we met again. Curiously, one day when I was looking through our address book, I saw his name and, on impulse, phoned him. It was quite out of character for me to do such a thing and I knew it was meant. We had a long talk which was important to us both.

I wanted to see him but felt very anxious before the actual meeting took place. How would I handle it? It would be quite different from talking on the phone which had an anonymous, disembodied quality, making it possible to speak without embarrassment. Should we talk about his illness? Avoid the subject altogether? Either way, he could be offended. Always too ready to weigh up the pros and cons, I felt indecisive, lacking in confidence.

I needn't have worried. Richie was completely natural, speaking frankly about his illness but not obsessed by it. We talked of many things, particularly his writing. He had written a short piece about his reaction when he was first told he was HIV positive which I admired greatly. His books are brilliant and we were anxious to persuade him to write the last book in his *Enchanted* trilogy.

After this first meeting we spoke regularly on the phone, often about the new book, and there were other meetings but, sadly, it soon became apparent that the final *Enchanted* book would never be written. Richie's energy was running out, sapped by recurrent chest infections and muscular pain. Nevertheless, his grip on life was tenacious and his spirit refused to give in. He lay on his couch, enjoying his magnificent fish tanks with their colourful, exotic fish and his dozens of hanging baskets full of glorious flowers. Plans continued to be made: a visit to the garden centre, to Harrods for a dear friend's present, a trip to Ireland, a new flat. Few could be realised, although he did manage to struggle to Harrods only to find they no longer stocked the present he had in mind.

Soon his chest became so bad that he had to go to hospital. We visited again and phoned often. What had once been a peripheral relationship was now very close. Whenever we went away, we lit a candle at the Catholic church. We have lit them all over the world. Our local priest was very helpful and I was grateful to him, as I am not a Catholic. He suggested that I should write Richie's name in his book for requesting prayers. I wrote: 'For Richie McMullen, who lives with AIDS with courage, and for his friend Bill Kirkpatrick, who gives great spiritual comfort to AIDS victims and their families'.

When he was in Westminster Hospital Richie said to me, 'The fight is on, Robina', and now in the London Lighthouse the fight continues. While he lives, Richie will not give in, become an invalid, eking out his existence with monotonous ease. He is as full of ideas as ever, chief among them at the moment this collection of pieces about AIDS from many contributors. I pray for him constantly and know that my life has been enriched by knowing him.

Robina Masters

The Pain, The Joy

I remember a time, the year before last, when I began to dread returning home and listening to my answering machine. Virtually every week I would find details of a funeral I was being asked to conduct for somebody who had died from an AIDS-related condition or news of a friend who had discovered he was HIV positive or had developed AIDS.

AIDS has affected me both as a man who has lost a fair number of friends to this virus and as a priest, ministering to those whose lives have been affected by it in various ways. The whole question of AIDS has affected me with an intensity that little else has done other than my vocation to the priesthood and my dedication to the struggle against fascism.

Knowing friends who have developed AIDS – friends I have known and loved, with whom I have had good times and to whom I've been able to turn for love and support in difficult times – has often made me ask 'Why them?' and 'Why not me?' Whatever the answer to such questions it is certainly not a question of justice, as some would have us believe. I know I am very fortunate not to be HIV positive – from the lifestyle I once lived I could easily be – and this awareness has had a profound effect on me.

This knowledge and the experience of loving friends and losing friends through this disease has given me a great sense of solidarity with all those affected by it: men and women, adults and children, in this country and overseas. A friend of mine, working in Africa, has just described to me her sharing with a 12-year-old girl who is HIV positive, who has already lost both her parents and her seven brothers and sisters and is now struggling to live with all

11

the implications this has for her. This solidarity has found expression in a wide variety of ways both in my personal life and in my life as a Christian priest. The solidarity of many people in offering love and support to those living with AIDS and HIV is a great inspiration and challenge. This is particularly true at those times one encounters hostility, prejudice and bigotry both in the media and in individuals with whom one comes into contact.

Some of the most memorable experiences I have had have been with people as they have been preparing for their deaths. Very often these have been people who, in their lives, have had no particular religious commitment. As the moment of their death has approached, they have displayed spiritual insights and awareness that have taught me a great deal. As they have spoken about their lives and their attitudes, I have so often been struck by the depth of caring and compassion, of fun and joy which they have communicated in the midst of their pain and fear. The care which people have taken over their own funeral arrangements and the funeral arrangements of loved ones has led to funeral services being real, and memorable, celebrations of life as well as times of grief, pain, anger and confusion. In the very midst of death, and the prospect of impending death, I have discovered a real sense of life and of hope, of solidarity and of love.

I have known a great deal of pain as I have seen people I have loved dying of this dreadful disease. I have also experienced a great pain because of the negative, condemnatory and patronising attitudes of those who claim, like me, to be following the God who is Love. Sometimes great protestations of love and concern are made about caring for people whatever their need may be; what I have often experienced has been a patronising condescension, and a reticence in compassion, caring and solidarity when faced with an actual person who might, for instance, have a 'prominent' position in a Christian community. I have often found it difficult to hold my head high as a Christian when

I have heard some of the uncaring, judgemental statements made by others who claim that allegiance. At times like these, I feel much more at one with those waiting at the bedside of a dying loved one and with those struggling to live with the implications of their own mortality than with those I may find myself kneeling beside at the altar rail, who have little to offer but words of condemnation and judgement. Many believers, Christians and others, have truly explored the implications of loving in their response to AIDS and HIV; many others have hardly begun.

In encountering AIDS and HIV, I have experienced some of the moments of deepest joy, love and pain in my life; some of the deepest spiritual experiences have sprung from these encounters. I have also experienced in the response of some people my moments of deepest shame and embarrassment in being a Christian.

Barry Naylor

Never Take Hope Away

The first recollection that I have of AIDS dates to a letter I read in an American gay magazine in 1981. In the 'Dear Doctor' column, a guy had written in saying he had just been diagnosed with a rare skin cancer and asking how he could conceal it. No mention of Kaposi's sarcoma; no mention of AIDS or even GRID (Gay-Related Immune Deficiency) as it was first called and, certainly, no mention of HIV (a virus waiting in the wings for its entrance in 1983).

I remember also having to write a short project during my final year as a medical student in 1983 and the topic I chose was the history of the fledgling AIDS epidemic. The entire medical literature on the subject took me one afternoon to read. By 1992, the volume of new information produced about HIV and AIDS overwhelms even the most diligent of medical journalists, and certainly, as a doctor, I can only keep up to date with certain aspects of the condition.

When I saw a post advertised in St Stephen's Hospital in London in 1986, I applied immediately, simply knowing that this was what I wanted to do. I had been working in a neurology unit in Yorkshire, mainly with patients with multiple sclerosis (MS). This stood me in good stead for dealing with a chronic progressive illness such as HIV and, even more so, with a condition of uncertain course and outcome. Both MS and HIV affect young adults and both result in stepwise or slowly progressive disability in many systems of the body. They are unpredictable in their course, although HIV, at least, has markers of progression – for example, T4 lymphocyte counts or AIDS-related infections. Finally, the available therapies for both conditions are few

14

and limited both in their effectiveness and their acceptability for many reasons.

There are several important differences between MS and HIV, however, and these give an insight into what has happened in the AIDS era and how the medical profession has reacted.

First, HIV is predominantly a sexually transmitted infection. The ability of society to deal with the diagnosis and treatment of sexually transmitted diseases has always been limited and HIV has catapulted back into the pre-antibiotic syphilis era as, once more, there is a commonly fatal sexually transmitted disease.

Secondly, HIV and AIDS, at the outset heterosexual worldwide, in the UK have predominantly affected gay men. As a gay man who happens to be a doctor, as opposed to a doctor who happens to be a gay man, it is perhaps difficult for me to be objective about what effects this has had on the course of the epidemic. It has resulted in unbelievable and revolutionary alterations in the pattern of care of chronic disease in young adults. The cohesion and dynamism of certain individuals and groups of gay men has led to a hitherto unseen openness and interaction between doctors, patients and carers which, I believe, has had immense benefits to all concerned.

Thirdly, of course, HIV has been a high-profile disease in society. Fuelled by a media fascination with any sexual behaviour that differs from the missionary position, fear and hatred initially flowed from the pens of most of the press. Those journalists who tried to report responsibly often failed due to the complexity of the issue and the fact that, as with MS, our knowledge about HIV and AIDS is sparse, but growing rapidly. In the early years of the epidemic, patients were frightened of being identified as carrying HIV or of being seen in the clinic, and rightly so considering the reactions they received which ranged from verbal abuse to fire bombs and instant dismissal from work. Some of those grotesque responses have lessened as time has passed but it is still far from easy to be openly HIV positive.

So what are the pleasures and difficulties for a doctor in caring for people who are HIV positive? I can only give my own view which, as I have had many friends and sexual partners and at least a few lovers with HIV or who have died of AIDS, is a relatively unusual one. What would I do if I didn't work in this field? I have no concept of another job which would give the same satisfaction, fascination, emotional kick and opportunities to achieve real change in the knowledge about, and treatment of, a particular condition.

At the moment, more than half my work is involved in developing new treatments and offering them to patients in the form of drug trials. A lot has been written and said about the balance between care and research. Many people have doubts and fears about research, but in fact research into the HIV epidemic has resulted in many changes to treatment. When I began to treat HIV in 1986, there were no licensed drugs available for cytomegalovirus (CMV), which causes blindness, life-threatening diarrhoea and many other serious conditions; now there are at least two drugs on the market that treat and prevent progression, at least for a prolonged period, of CMV. Also until 1986, no drugs had been shown to have any effect on HIV itself whereas now at least three drugs are being used which slow progression and reduce mortality – and many more are in the pipeline. The role of prophylaxis, using drugs to prevent pneumonia in AIDS, is well established and has undoubtedly had benefits for those at risk of such conditions.

However, this improvement in the drug armamentarium is often a double-edged sword, and I have seen the emergence of conditions which were uncommon when I first started. Lymphoma, a cancer of the lymph systems, is now common and lacks effective treatment in late-stage HIV. This sometimes makes me ask 'Is it not better to die with

16

an opportunistic infection early on rather than survive to get something even worse later?' But I believe that my role is to provide choice and information and not to dictate therapy. I believe that the doctor today should not be a paternalistic figure who dispenses pearls of wisdom but rather an adviser, confidante and, above all, friend of his patient. I once worked for a neurology consultant who said, 'Never take away a patient's hope; it isn't your right or role to do so', and this remains one of the tenets of my care. Of course, it's always important to be truthful and honest. Many doctors skirt around the issues of deterioration in health, death and dying; issues which raise their head more frequently as time progresses. This is the easy option and is a mistake. If a patient comes to you with a severely damaged immune system, however well they are, to ignore the fact that they are likely to get ill in the near future is, I believe, absolutely the wrong thing to do.

When patients first see me out on the gay scene, in a club or a bar, doing exactly the same as they are doing, they often react with surprise. I make a point of never acknowledging a patient first, unless I know him as a friend, for reasons of confidentiality and also because I try to maintain at least some time free from work. But many of my patients *are* my friends and vice versa and, for me, HIV has become so much a part of life that I sometimes fail to recognise that most people outside the gay scene have little knowledge of or interest in the subject.

Dealing with the illness, dying and death of many people, especially of your own age and social group, is something that few have to deal with until they are in their 70s and 80s and this is one of the greatest strains of all. However, every day I see someone who says something that makes me realise that I wouldn't be happy doing anything else.

Mike Youle

Changing My Views

Richie, you ask how this viral infection has affected my life. It's hard to know where to begin because it has affected me in a multitude of ways, both professionally and personally.

I think back to all the things I was taught at college when I was training as an occupational therapist and laugh to myself at how the virus has challenged traditional ways of working.

'It's not professional to cry with a client.' What is professional, I ask you, when you're sitting quietly with someone who's dying and they tell you that, despite all they are about to lose, it feels okay because they have met some wonderful people who have enriched their life?

'It's not professional to discuss personal details about yourself.' Tell that to someone who is expected to talk about their innermost thoughts and fears to a complete stranger. Richie, you wouldn't have let me get away with saying nothing and I thank you for that! Do you remember our first session together? I remember it well, not least because I didn't mention occupational therapy once, the very reason why I was supposed to be sitting in your flat. However, it was a wonderful afternoon, and by the end of it we had discussed everything from sexuality to death to the best cigars to smoke. It didn't seem to matter that I had no idea whether you could get in and out of the bath on your own.

'You shouldn't give your home phone number to a client.' On the odd occasion when I have felt it necessary to break this rule, I feel it has not backfired on me. I've dragged myself out of bed in the middle of the night (no mean feat for someone who seems to need 12 hours' sleep a night just to be civil the next day!); I've stayed up all night when necessary and it has been a privilege to do this. I will always cherish those special moments spent with people.

Richie, some people, not least of all you, have taught me so much. Your unwritten rule to yourself is that you must not receive without giving. You have shared so much of your life with me and, through this, have enabled me to grow. I have learnt that, through adversity, there is always a light and it is up to all of us to create that light, however long the tunnel may seem. Sometimes it has felt like I've been stuck in that tunnel, particularly when, despite all the best intentions, I feel totally powerless in a given situation. Yet, perhaps in our own way we get there in the end (a lesson, I fear, British Rail has not yet learnt!). This reminds me of a time when someone special, who was on *his* last lap, was desperately trying to force yet more medication down his throat. His light was the promise of a sip of champagne from a teaspoon after each pill. Somehow or other the pills went down!

I have never ceased to be amazed by the strength the virus has instilled in people. Imagine the courage it takes to tell your parents (on your last lap) that not only are you gay, but you also have AIDS. What a time to risk rejection from those so close to you. I was privileged to witness such a scene and it has taught me to follow my feelings and follow through what I believe is right for me. I am learning that perhaps it is not my problem if others cannot cope with my honesty.

Richie, last week someone asked me after their partner's funeral where I thought she might have gone to. I simply answered that I did not know but, wherever it was, she would be joining a lot of other very special people. I have learnt, through working with people with the virus, that you do not have to come up with all the answers; sometimes there are no answers; sometimes it's enough just to share your own thoughts.

Richie, as energy was being drained out of you by this virus, you surrounded yourself with more life. Your flat became a haven for fish and plants. (Do you remember telling staff at the Mildmay how they had not prepared their fish tank properly?) The pleasure that has brought you in the past months has taught me that perhaps I have taken good health for granted. Maybe I do not have to set my personal goals so high. I now appreciate nature more than I ever thought possible. Mind you, it's hard to hold on to this thought when the squirrels are digging up my newly planted bulbs!

So, Richie, you asked how the virus had touched me. I hope this gives you a small insight into the way it has affected my life. I owe thanks to people like yourself for giving me so much and allowing me to learn valuable lessons while I am still healthy enough to put them into practice.

You will be with me always.

Deb Gilmore

How Has HIV/AIDS Affected Me?

I moved down to London from Geordieland in 1988 to find out more about nursing people with HIV infection. At that time some of my nursing colleagues expressed vehement, prejudiced views about HIV/AIDS – for example, talking of HIV being 'God's wrath on gays'. I did not feel equipped with either knowledge or experience to challenge such comments as I would today. However, I was sure that they were unacceptable.

In a personal capacity, I found the judgemental, ignorant comments offensive as two of my closest friends were, and still are, a gay couple. I also questioned their professional philosophy, as I believed that people came into nursing to nurse people irrespective of colour, sexuality or illness. However, I soon became aware that this HIV/AIDS was very different from any other disease.

HIV/AIDS challenges two of our society's biggest taboos: sexuality and death and dying; HIV/AIDS also presented me with the first of many personal and professional challenges that I am still facing. Before working with people with AIDS, I had experienced death and loss both personally and in my nursing career, but I had never had the opportunity to acknowledge the impact that it had on my life. Nurses are expected to 'cope with' death with very little training or support; during my three years' nursing training we had only two lectures on the care of the dying. On hospital wards, when someone dies, the nursing team seemed to do its utmost to hide the fact as though it were some kind of a mistake or failure, ushering patients into their rooms with some excuse as to why they should keep away from the kitchen – in case they become aware that someone has died in the room next door.

Thomas Macauley Ward at St Stephen's Hospital, London, where I became involved in caring for people with AIDS in 1988, was one of the first designated HIV units and so patients were receiving the latest medical treatment. I was caring for patients who knew far more about their illness than I did, and I learnt a lot from them. The approach to care was holistic, acknowledging the social and psychological as well as the physical needs of the patients, and also acknowledging the needs of the partner and family. As the majority of patients at this time were gay men, it was very important to acknowledge and support the lover. I have had the privilege of observing and being part of caring for people whose unconditional love for their partner was, for me, inspirational – the kind of gay relationship that the general public rarely gets to hear about.

I also feel very privileged to have had some contact with some of the awesome voluntary organisations established by gay men infected and affected by HIV – such as Body Positive, Terrence Higgins Trust and London Lighthouse. The media have been quick to criticise such organisations, but have never given them the public recognition that they deserve for their dedicated commitment in raising public awareness about HIV.

Through my work with people with AIDS, I have had to look at my own life – my relationships, my own mortality – and I feel that I have grown so much and have learnt to be more honest with myself and to understand what being a nurse really is. I remember when I first started on TMac (as Thomas Macauley is known) feeling so uncomfortable when a patient called Frank wanted to talk about his impending death. 'I'd like lots of white lilies and Pink Floyd at my funeral.' I had to make an excuse and leave the room as I had a lump the size of a tennis ball in my throat. That weekend, as part of a counselling course run by the Terrence Higgins Trust, I spent two days looking at death and dying – including my past experiences of death, my own mortality, planning my own funeral, looking at my fears and fantasies about death. When I went back to work on Monday, I went to Frank's room and was able to sit with him while he spoke of his funeral and impending death.

Through HIV/AIDS, I have learnt many things. Recently, when one of my best friends, Sue, was ill with cancer, I could be there – especially at the time of her death – ensuring that she died with dignity and was the Sue that I knew so well and loved, and I was instrumental in planning her memorial service.

My friends often ask, 'Doesn't it depress you working with dying people all the time?' I think one of the main things that I have learnt is that HIV is about living as well as dying and that it is the *quality*, not the *quantity*, of life that is important.

I have learnt to acknowledge the relationships that I am privileged to have made. One of my most rewarding nursing experiences was saying goodbye to Chris, a patient that I had nursed for some time, just before he lapsed into unconsciousness prior to death. I said goodbye and acknowledged what a privilege it had been to know and nurse him, and I accepted his thanks for my care. I went on my days off knowing I wouldn't see Chris again, but that I had no unfinished business.

I sometimes go to memorial services to say goodbye to patients because I feel it is important to validate my feelings: I am Fiona, the nurse, but also Fiona, the person, who feels and cares deeply, and HIV/AIDS has allowed me to do this in a professional capacity.

I am now privileged to work at London Lighthouse in an informal, but very professional, environment, where we refer to people as residents, not as patients to get away from institutionalised care. Care of residents here is individualised, honest, non-judgemental; the organisation's philosophy is that death is very much part of life. When someone dies, we acknowledge it respectfully by lighting a candle at the nurse's station and downstairs at reception for 24 hours, and we tell people what the candle signifies.

I love my job – with its sadness and laughter – and three years on, I am still learning so much about life from people affected by HIV. I feel it is appropriate to finish with a poem which I and other participants were given at a workshop run by Body Positive in 1988.

> Because each of you is you
> I will not forget
> the way that we were

> > Nor will I forget how
> > we were together
> > for such a short time
> > in my life

> > > And each of you
> > > has given something to me
> > > that I cannot forget

> > > > You have given me the
> > > > experience
> > > > of being alive with you
> > > > and knowing and encountering
> > > > the Spirit within us
> > > > and between us

> > > > And gave all that I could
> > > > though I wish it had been more
> > > > but I know and you know
> > > > what prevented and allowed
> > > > our greater living together

> > > So to each of you
> > > I want to say thank you
> > > thank you for allowing me
> > > to see into your lives
> > > and to experience what
> > > only those whom you love
> > > experience and know

How Has HIV/AIDS Affected Me?

I shall not forget you
since you have shown me
who you are in such a short time
nor can I be the less for it.

Anon

Fiona Talby

I Don't Understand Aids

I don't understand AIDS. Not conceptually, intellectually or emotionally. Only in some small way mechanically do I begin to grasp the 'what' and the 'how'; the 'why' escapes me completely. The 'who' and the 'when' is what I really know about at that very deep gut level of painful feelings: anger, sadness, frustration, hopelessness, impotence, disbelief.

To most of those living in this one-bus-a-day picturesque village in the north of England, AIDS is something we see on television and read about in the newspaper. It's not part of our reality.

Then Richie bravely and gently told me he was HIV positive and reality caught up with me. My friend, my soulmate, my brother was saying that he might not be able to be there for me forever, and that no amount of my being there for him would make the slightest difference to this mystery that had invaded his body.

I'm a fast learner when I want to be and I began the long and painful process of learning about AIDS – long because like a lot of people I'm quite good at putting off things I would rather not have to do; painful because of what I learnt.

I learnt that there is shamefully little money for AIDS research or treatment.

I learnt that, for most people, AIDS is something that only happens to people in Third World countries and, therefore doesn't need to concern us deeply.

Worse still, I learnt that some people, even now, feel that AIDS cannot happen to heterosexual people but only to 'them' so that makes it okay.

But the most distressing thing I learnt was that some

people are convinced that AIDS is the 'divine retribution' of God. What kind of God this could be escapes me. It isn't the loving God I know.

Do you get the impression I'm angry?

'Angry' would be an underestimation of what I feel. But even as I move on from this anger, so the reality of AIDS moves on and consumes another of my family and more and more of my family of humanity.

Some time during 1983, when Richie and I were sharing our hopes, dreams and aspirations for the future and planning how we intended to go about achieving our goals, parallel but separately, he wrote this poem for me. I have lived the poem ever since with grateful thanks and will go on doing so with love.

> That bit of you
> you gave to me
> I offer back
> that bit of me
> the mutual and
> the separate we
> that grows and
> knows we shall
> be free.
>
> See the wall
> paint it red
> no more hiding
> in books and
> bed
> see the colour
> know yourself
> know that it's
> the shade of wealth
>
> Sculpt yourself
> from inside out
> close your ears

to 'there's no way out'
you are the artist
now be the clay
produce yourself
be that way.

Helen Francis

Somebody Loves Me

'She's known as Our Lady of the Goats.'
　'Any good reason?'
　'The goats.'
　'She's also a recluse.'
As I drove Danny down the track, the valley was sharp, narrow and thickly wooded and the sun was sinking in a crimson ball. Danny hadn't seen his mother for five years. They had corresponded occasionally, but that was it, for Mrs Hegarty had no phone. She'd lived on the farm all her life, seeing only her husband and Danny and an elderly labourer called Rooney. But now her husband and Rooney were long dead. Danny had left home when he was 15 and gone to London; all she had left were the goats and the tumbledown house.

Danny was ill. AIDS was consuming him and he was wheelchair-bound now, his bones brittle and the chest infections never far way. But this trip to the west of Ireland had slipped from a dream to an obsession to a practicality, and we had spent the last two days idyllically, driving along the lanes and watching the ocean and spending the nights in remote guest houses. Last night we had stayed in a squat stone building high on a cliff-top. The wind had torn at the surf, bringing it crashing in plumes over the rocks: 'I wish I could die now,' he had whispered, 'it seems the right moment.'
　'What about your Mum?' I had asked, holding him tight in my arms.
　'She was always a harridan. She'll probably nag me to death. That's not a good way to go.' He looked down at the boiling waves and laughed his wheezy laugh.

'There's no one in.'

The yard was as empty as the house, the byre ghostly with its still redolent smell of cow.

'She'll come.'

'Not even a light.'

Danny looked at his watch. 'She'll be in bed by now.'

'It's only six.'

'She gets up at dawn.'

We had been delayed by the afternoon sun and a field of clover. Again I'd held him in my arms, my cheek pressed into the sweet earth that would soon absorb him. 'I'm not being burnt to a cinder,' he had told me. 'Find me a grave in a country churchyard.'

After a struggle with recalcitrant vicars, I had found one in Sussex. Danny had been pleased with its ivy-trailing desolation.

'You'll come, won't you? You'll come and stand by my grave.'

'Every day,' I had assured him ironically.

'You lying bastard,' he had replied.

I knocked again and thought I heard a movement. Then the bolts rattled and the door opened an inch. There was no light, not even the flicker of a candle.

'Yes?'

Danny said nothing, which was a pity because I was totally unprepared. Somehow I had expected him to greet her and, while I didn't think they'd fall on each other's necks, I felt there would at least be mumbled communication. But there was nothing.

'It's Danny,' I said woodenly.

'Who?'

'Danny.'

'Danny?' I couldn't see her face and her voice was rough and dry.

'Your son.'

There was a long silence. 'Yes?'

Yes what, I wondered. 'Can we come in?'

The door opened a fraction. 'That's not my son.'

If only Danny would *say* something, I thought, angrily now. Had he been struck dumb? 'It is.'

'My son's not a cripple.'

'He's been ill.'

'What with?'

'AIDS.'

'What's that?'

'A virus.'

The door opened another crack. 'Danny?'

At last he spoke. 'Mother.'

'What are you doing here?'

'Thought I'd come.'

'Who's your friend?'

'That's Colin.'

'You'd better come in.'

The hallway smelt of the same earth as the fields and there was something else overlaying it – something animal. Was it goat? There was a scurrying, clattering movement. Were there goats in the house?

She led us down a narrow passage, Danny's wheelchair barely clearing the walls, and into a kitchen. Mrs Hegarty snapped on the light and I saw her properly for the first time. She gave me a shock because I had been expecting someone very old. Well, she *was* old but I had no means of guessing her age for her face, long and aquiline like Danny's, was completely unmarked. She had huge eyes, again like Danny's, but his face was wasted and hers was full, unwrinkled, unsagging. Around her the kitchen was bleak and desolate, with a range that threw out little heat. Curled up against the tepid warmth was a kid; its eyes stared up at us helplessly.

The kitchen was painted blue but the paint was coming off. On the dilapidated shelves were a few chipped cups

31

and plates and in the centre of the room was a big scrubbed table with four chairs around it. There was a cupboard – it could have been a larder – but nothing else. The room frightened me with its spartan bleakness.

'I've not got much in the house.'

The kid moved and then resettled, making an anxious sigh.

'That's all right.' Danny was silent again and I looked at my watch. It was only ten past six. What were we going to do? Suddenly the evening seemed an eternity.

'I can do bacon. An egg and a bit of fried bread.'

'Ideal.' I cleared my throat, looking vengefully at Danny, willing him to share the responsibility of conversation.

She began to move around, placing each object of food on a tin draining board. Outside there was no wind, and an enormous stillness filled the room which was barely broken when Mrs Hegarty spoke.

'How did you get ill, Danny?'

'It just came.' His voice was neutral.

'Will you get better?'

'No.'

'That why you came?'

'Sort of.'

'Just dropped in?'

'Yes.'

'You'll be off in the morning?'

'Probably.'

She looked at him properly for the first time and then muttered. 'I'll outlive you all then.'

She served the meal and I suddenly realised I was ravenous, but Danny ate little. There was no conversation but gradually I realised it didn't matter. I was beginning to find an increasing peace in this almost empty space. The table, the chairs, the food, the kid, the range, the sink and the two cupboards. No more. No less. Peace.

'Mother—' He spoke for the first time in what must have been ten minutes. Maybe more.

'Danny.'

'Can I sleep in your room for the night?'

I froze, but quickly the resentment turned to acceptance. After all, we'd leave in the morning.

She laughed lightly. 'I've got another couple of kids in there.'

'Does it matter?' he asked.

'No.'

He turned to me. 'You come too, Colin.'

'Me? All of us?' It was ludicrous. Were we all to sleep in one bed?

She made tea, strong and bitter. Then, despite the early hour, she showed us to another small, almost empty room and I helped her put mattresses on the floor.

'You sleep downstairs then?' I asked.

'The top's empty now.'

'Empty?'

'I sold everything. Now I've just got the things I need.' She looked at me properly for the first time. 'I'll die soon. The dead don't need knick-knacks.' She looked at Danny and he laughed as I helped him out of the wheelchair and on to a mattress, covering him with a couple of rough blankets, which smelt of mothballs. Made a change from goat, I thought.

The kids came in, slightly larger than the one by the range in the kitchen, and they climbed on to her bed, lying on the dowdy eiderdown.

She stood there, watching us for a while. Maybe she was wondering why Danny had laughed. Then he said.

'We're cluttered out with stuff.'

'Where are you now?' she asked, yawning.

'Fulham.'

Mrs Hegarty went out of the room and came back wearing a nightgown. She got into bed and switched out the light. Later on I heard her making sleeping sounds.

'Danny.' I whispered. 'I feel at peace here. Do you?'

'Yes.' He paused and then his voice reached me through the darkness, 'She's just got space, hasn't she? My mother. She's taken everything away. Maybe when she dies she'll have nothing. Just bare rooms. That's the way they'll find her. In a bare room.'

'Were you happy?'

'When?'

'With her – as a child.'

'I think so. It was hard. I worked and went to school. Weekends were much the same. Except there was no school. Just Dad and Mum and Rooney, and the cows then, of course.'

'Didn't you have any friends?'

'No,' he said baldly, but without self-pity.

'What made you decide to get away?'

'Something in me. Something I needed. The streets.'

That's where we'd met. On the streets. He was a rent boy and I was his client. Then the professional relationship stopped – and *we* began.

'But I knew all the time,' Danny said.

'Knew what?'

'Someone loved me.'

'Her?'

'Yes.'

'Why didn't you come back to see her – keep in contact?'

'Don't know. It was enough to know it, I s'pose.'

We lay in silence for a moment. There were no curtains to the window and the stars winked bright against a jet black sky.

'*Will* we leave tomorrow?' I asked.

'Yes.'

'Go back home?'

'Please.'

'And her?'

'I'll not see her again.'

'So why come?'

'To find out.'

34

'What?'

'If she loves me still.'

'And does she?'

'Yes.'

'What about me?' A sense of desolation welled up in me.

'You?'

'I love you.'

'I know you do.' His voice warmed me again. 'It's different,' he added.

'How?' I demanded.

'You love me as I am, Colin. I wanted to find out if Mum would love me as the person I've become – not what I was. Her little boy.'

'And does she?'

'I think she does.'

I slept deeply and woke in the grey dawn. When I turned to Danny's mattress I panicked because he was no longer there. Then I saw the two of them by the window. She was propping him up and he had his arms around her, his thin legs trailing behind him. Someone loves me. I felt nothing but joy for both of them as they stared out at the shadowy landscape of trees and mist and shifting substance. It was not real yet, as if the valley was being born. Mother and son watched the foetal development with concentration and awe.

She let him go, I thought, let him go to the city and the streets because she knew she couldn't clip his wings.

The kids got off the bed and nuzzled at their legs. As they did so, Danny turned and smiled at me.

'Come on,' he said. 'She can't hold me up forever.'

'You'd better take him,' said Mrs Hegarty softly. 'He's not much of a weight but I'm an old woman. I'll make tea.'

As she passed Danny to me there was something in Mrs Hegarty's eyes that moved me profoundly. It was as if she was finally giving him away.

35

'You were right to believe in her,' I whispered to him and kissed his cold cheek.

Anthony Masters

I Will Keep The Light

How has AIDS changed my life? 'Completely' is the short answer and if I try to expand on it too much, I will be in grave danger of sounding trite. Through working with people with AIDS, I have discovered, to my surprise, a faith that runs very deep. Faith in a higher power certainly, and in the spark of that same power which exists in human beings – the power to fight for life, to struggle to realise our greatest potential, the power to love, dream and find moments of happiness against all odds, and the power it takes to surrender to the inevitable when the time is right.

Richie, when I walked into your basement nest, I found a valued friend. You had responded to the challenge of your illness by writing your life story, sharing what you had learnt professionally and personally. The writing had stopped by the time we met; you were already too weak for that, but how you talked. You told stories; you explained; you gave of yourself, your wisdom, your experience, your pain and your humour; and you accepted whatever I could give you, sometimes with difficulty but always with grace. You and I were always talking about food. Whatever the conversation, whether it was about the legs on the players at Wimbledon, or about love or death, somehow a flavour or a smell would be recalled and we'd be off. Remembering meals, fantasising about meals, even planning menus for meals which we knew we'd never really cook together, but it was fun to play. The last time I saw you, a few weeks before you died, we planned a meal, just a simple one, and discussed the wine – red Italian, I think – then we said 'goodbye'. The memory of all those pretend meals will nourish me for a long time to come.

I also remember David, fighting his way tooth and nail back from the edge of death, practising the violin again for a few more weeks before it got too heavy; Grant, insisting on withdrawing from morphine in the hospital so that he could be clear-headed for his family's visit. When he knew the end was very near, he threw away all but the most essential drugs, called for champagne and insisted that everybody party.

The knowledge of this life-threatening illness, which is mainly contracted through the beautiful, and once simple, act of making love, has changed my life. Finding the special friendship of Richie and of Grant has changed my life. . . . and the experiences of being allowed by each of them to share part of their respective journeys has transformed it . . . and so has the sadness of missing them now. Through them and others, my way of working has changed and broadened so I hope I can pass on some of the gifts of understanding which they left me. I know I will keep the light which they brought into my life – for ever.

Chrissie Richman

The Doctor's Tale

Doctors have an uneasy relationship with illness: we are supposed to be against it but, at the same time, we have an interest in its existence – where would we be without it? As someone whose personal and professional life has been transformed by HIV infection, this somewhat disturbing thought occasionally puzzles me. If HIV infection has, indeed, played an important part in my life, how has it come about and what have I learnt from it?

At first, few of us realised what those reports from the US meant and, in the early days of my involvement with people with HIV back in 1985, I would have been unable to imagine what was to follow. For better or for worse we, the privileged children of the affluent developed world, have found ourselves in the midst of the turmoil of a historical period which had reminded us painfully of the need to confront the unmentionable, of the limitations of medicine, and of the social and economic impact of epidemics. The combination of social, medical and political issues involved has been one of the reasons why so many of us have gravitated towards working with HIV-related problems but, deep down, there may have been more personal motives; in my case, I can say that the fact that people who were close to me became ill played an important part.

What have I learnt so far? It may seem an unnecessary luxury to take a constructive, perhaps even upbeat, attitude in the face of so much pain, but I am aware of the need to reflect and to attempt to understand where my work is taking me. At an individual, personal level, the main lesson has been the discovery of the strength, serenity and humour with which the majority of people with HIV cope with the adversity that often follows. How much this is the result of the person's own efforts, and how much the consequence of support by families, friends and others, varies in each case. Will I be able to confront mortality when my time comes with the same dignity and self-control?

In parallel with the discovery of how much people can do for themselves had come the awareness of the limitations of what we, the doctors, can or should do. I do not simply mean that treatments are ineffective or inadequate – while this is sometimes the case, much has been learnt and achieved in the way of medical interventions in the last few years. I mean that the role of doctors as technical advisers, as those experts that can supply you with the information you need to make a decision, rather than as all-powerful figures that know best, has started to become the rule, rather than the exception. In my view, this is, without doubt, a good thing, not just because it redresses the balance in the traditional doctor-patient relationship, ensuring that the autonomy and control of the ill person is preserved, but also because it accepts the reality of the incompleteness of what the doctor knows, even at a technical level.

In a more general sense, the way the medical approach to the care of people with HIV has evolved in many developed countries has begun to fulfil the hopes that many of us entertained in those heady days at medical school when, in our naivety, we argued for a medicine which took into account social and psychological factors, not only as possible causes of disease, but also as its likely consequences. HIV infection has made it routine for physicians to talk to epidemiologists, psychiatrists and social scientists, and for basic science workers to consult experts in ethics; perhaps this is another reason why it seems so difficult to get away from working with HIV-related problems. This holistic approach to the care of people with illnesses may be the most important lesson that HIV infection can teach medicine.

Pepe Catalan

The End of Autumn

You were sitting in a wheelchair
by the open french doors
your cigar smoke moving out into October air
to grey sky and leafless trees
to the end of autumn.

We spoke of the sadness of a mind
still fertile with ideas,
at least six more books there
now never to be born,
your body unable to complete their creation.

We spoke of ways you could ask others
to nurture the ideas alive in your mind
conceived but not grown.

Delivered to the care of your friends
and those whose lives you touched,
fostered,
they are not stillborn
but live

Which is why I write this instead of you.

Noreen Ramsay

Full Care and Attention

In 1988 I started work on Thomas Macauley Ward at St Stephen's Hospital. I knew nothing about HIV and AIDS but, as a Sister of Charity involved with caring for people in any kind of need, I was willing to give it a try. Our congregation was, at that time, re-assessing our work and looking at certain needs in other areas and responding to the 'needs of our time'. In a discussion with my Provincial Superior, I had mentioned that I felt AIDS was an area that I could be involved in as a nurse and that is how I first became involved at St Stephen's.

I had worked for twelve years on a coronary care unit and for some years in homes for the elderly so I was familiar enough with death, the process of dying and the care involved; care not only for the patients but also for the families and loved ones. However, I was apprehensive about how I would cope with young people dying. When I visited the ward for the first time, I immediately detected a good atmosphere and I was very excited about starting work the following week.

The patients were, for the most part, male and homosexual but we also had several female patients. There was a great emphasis on living, although the quality of life, for some, was poor. The approach to nursing on the ward was very different; for the first time in my experience, the patient was the boss! Patients were very involved in their own treatment and care and discussed at length with their doctors the treatment that was available, the side effects and the risks. A doctor was present on the ward all day and this was very reassuring for the patients.

The patients got up when they wanted to in the morning. The days of turfing patients out of bed at 7 am were over and no one bothered about when the beds were made. It might be 7 pm when a patient felt ready to get out of bed and then he might want to go out for meal or to the theatre or a club. Patients had their treatment when it was convenient for them; early if they wanted to go out or later if they wanted to lie in. It was all very civilised, I thought.

There was also plenty of time to talk to the group of patients a nurse was allocated to care for each day. The whole patient was cared for physically, mentally, psychologically and spiritually, and the nurse got to know her patients in order to give them the best possible attention. A multidisciplinary team met weekly to discuss patients' needs and make referrals for further care when necessary. Spiritual help was also available to patients who wanted it and, often, the chaplain on his rounds would talk over with a patient what funeral arrangements or the kind of service he would like. He would also be there to support family and friends during this time.

The number of varying illnesses and conditions of people with AIDS who are admitted to hospital never ceases to amaze me. I find it incredible that young people can cope with being so ill and having so many problems in their short lives and still be able to laugh and joke. Support from partners and family sometimes falls short but, then again, those who have the support are very lucky and it is most edifying to see.

The way in which young men and women face death is often incredible and there were many instances when I was undeniably moved by their openness and strength of character in their preparation for death. So often we have picked hymns together for their funeral and, with great clarity, prepared the whole funeral service, writing down every detail of the arrangements and celebrations to follow. This can sometimes be difficult for a partner but many would admit that it was easier to make funeral arrangements when the instructions were already there, written by the loved one prior to his death.

On one occasion Chris, a patient, asked me how long he had got and when I said that I wasn't God and couldn't say, he replied, 'Well, ask Him then – you work for Him'. Chris persisted in his question and I replied that I didn't think he would be with us in three weeks' time. He had all his affairs in order but there was one friend he dearly wanted to see. We set about contacting his friend, who came to say his farewell and, a week later, Chris was still with us. When I went into his room, the first thing he said was, 'You said I wouldn't be here today and I am'. (He was very ill but also very bright and had a great sense of humour.) Chris had done all he wanted to do and there was no hope of him improving so he wanted to die. We had long chats during the night and we prayed. I was edified by his faith and the content of his prayer. Eventually Chris slept and was still sleeping when I went off duty next morning. That night, when I came on duty, Chris was unconscious and his wish for death was fulfilled in the early hours of the morning. He was peaceful and all the stress and pain had gone from his face. His emaciated body, half the size it was when I first knew him, was now free from pain. His parents had sat by his bedside throughout the night. I felt sad at losing a friend, but there was joy, too, as his weeks of preparation for death had now ended with a dignity I had not witnessed before.

There are times when carers on the ward feel distress and upset, especially when there are two or even three deaths on the same day or in the same week. People have their own support systems very often and support from colleagues on the ward is always evident – that is what makes Thomas Macauley Ward the place it is. It has been known for well patients to render support and concern when patients are dying. They can also be a support to the family and friends over a cup of coffee in the day room.

My support comes mainly from my community so I am

ever-grateful for their love and understanding. To live with a group of people who are supportive and available when I am under stress or have had a heavy day is marvellous. One particular incident – when I had a needle-stick injury at work – taught me a great deal about myself and those who supported me through it. It also helped me to understand a little of what patients feel and experience when they are awaiting the result of an HIV test or an AIDS diagnosis and the support they need at such a critical time. I feel deeply for other nurses in the same position having, perhaps, to go back to a one-bedroom flat or to the nurses' home with no one to talk to and how incredibly lonely they must feel.

My own faith helps me greatly too and my belief in God has been strengthened on many occasions when I witnessed death in all its variations. I feel saddened at times when I hear patients asking why God has done this to them; they seem to equate pain and suffering with punishment for sin. At other times, they will say 'Why me? I have never hurt anyone in my life'.

Patients often ask me to pray for them or with them or even to light a candle in church for them. Prayer strengthens me and, somehow, it helps put things in perspective. During Mass, I often mention the names of patients on the ward and commend them to His love and mercy. From there, too, I'm strengthened and renewed to face the next day and to thank God for the day that has been. Each day has its own joys and sorrows; no matter how depressing or sad, there is always a joyful moment and I try to find that and hang on to it for that day. The care and attention given by partners and friends are far more than duty demands. They often remain with very ill partners and friends throughout the night and during the day for weeks at a time. They shop and cook for them, wash clothes and care for them as well as a wife or husband care for each other. I can truly say that I have not witnessed such care and attention in my other fields of nursing as I have on TMac.

That, too, is why I have so much respect for the patients
and friends of TMac Ward.

Sister Pearl Lenihan

Pain Shared

It was late August. As I walked down the hall towards the front door I could see two figures through the glass. Suzy had brought her boyfriend with her, the West Indian actor with whom her life had become so emotionally enmeshed and about whom I had become increasingly intrigued. She had telephoned out of the blue five weeks earlier asking if I would bless her house. When we had finished the ritual we sat down with a coffee. She began talking about her lover, a guy with whom she had a tempestuous and confusing relationship. Her descriptions had been so vivid, and their encounters so bizarre, he a New-Age adherent with a history of gay encounters, she a born-again Christian escaping a Catholic childhood and later years of alcohol abuse and domestic violence. This particular afternoon she was coming to visit me, and she'd brought him with her. I opened the door. Suzy introduced me to John. My attraction to him was instant.

We met for an hour, and I listened as each expressed frustration and misunderstanding to the other about their relationship. They were hooked, couldn't let go, needed each other too much, and yet couldn't survive so much intimacy. Suzy needed to rescue John from his homosexuality; John needed . . . well, I'm still not sure.

After they left, I felt excited and disturbed. John was such a charismatic figure, full of energy, humour and sexual presence. I wanted to meet him again, but I had rarely felt confident enough to make a first move. Dare I make contact with him and invite him out? Would he be interested in someone like me? I telephoned him the next day and said I'd like to meet. We talked for an hour and agreed to go to the theatre the following weekend. I felt triumphant, but arrived home late that night to find a message from John saying that he'd had second thoughts and had decided that it was unwise to meet. I felt devastated and spent a restless, sleepless night.

In the morning I listened to his message again. The finality I had heard the night before sounded less absolute: 'Ring if you think this doesn't seem right'. I decided a phone call was worth the risk of finding a rejecting person at the other end. But he wasn't rejecting. Neither, after a night's sleep, had he changed his mind. We talked; I said I might write to him, and he said he enjoyed receiving letters.

For the next seven days I reflected on what had happened and wrote a very safe, newsy, chatty letter to John. To my surprise, he replied a week later with a far-from-negative message written inside a card of Monet's 'White Nenuphars'. The card seemed to have been carefully chosen, the symbolism of the bridge intentional. I sent back a picture of an open gate. To my amazement, he telephoned as soon as he received my card.

And so we started to meet. Initially I was over-anxious, ridiculously on my best behaviour, nervous as an adolescent on his first date wanting to do everything right. We met at weekends and went for leisurely country walks. We met in cafés in town and went to movies. I allowed flexibility to grow in my normally rigid pattern of life in response to his quest for spontaneity. I was also hopelessly over-optimistic. I had no doubt that this relationship would develop into something that would bring me everything I had ever dreamt of.

One Saturday evening in late November, after we had spent the afternoon together, John told me that the previous week he had gone for an AIDS test, and the result was positive. I felt devastated. John wanted to catch the tube home, alone. I didn't want to be left alone at that moment, and persuaded him to go for a meal. I asked questions about his health and lifestyle; he answered, reluctantly.

Eventually we talked about other topics, paid the bill, and made our separate ways home.

At home I wanted to scream, but there were other residents in the house. I walked down to the local church which was unlocked and empty. I paced about in the darkness, shouting and screaming, stamping and kicking my feet and thumping the pillars and chairs with my fists. 'Why? Why him and why me, just when, for the first time in my life I had taken an initiative of courageous dimensions, for me, and invited someone out? It was so cruel and unfair. Unfair!' I wept and groaned, furious with John for having been so careless with himself, sorry for myself for having been played such a cruel trick, demanding of God to know why – why had it turned out this way? Why, just when things seemed to be going so well, had I been dealt such a cruel blow?

I went home and cried myself into a restless sleep. I appeared at work the next morning looking distressed and feeling tender and vulnerable. I asked my colleagues for patience and understanding. Tears were close to the surface, but I made it through the day, just holding myself together. I returned home and started phoning sympathetic friends.

Over the following weeks John began to cut himself off; every time I phoned I was told that he was unavailable. I grew daily more frustrated and anxious, wondering what I had done that was making John reject me. I was to learn later that this was his way of dealing with crises and that the confident, smiling, extrovert that I had met that first, fateful afternoon was also strongly defended, protecting himself ruthlessly against unwanted attention and uncomfortable feelings.

For the next four years we had a difficult, intermittent relationship. There were lengthy periods when we were separated from each other because the pressure of feelings had grown too great for John to cope with. He spent several months working in Germany and I visited him there twice. The visits were not easy for either of us; John was uneasy about having me invade his territory and an area of his life which he had kept quite separate. On both visits, my presence became too uncomfortable for him after two or three days and we lapsed into an intolerable silence. He then spent several months in Singapore. We corresponded with each other occasionally while he was there and I began to accept that the hopes and dreams I had entertained in relation to John would never be fulfilled.

Then one cold December Monday morning two weeks before Christmas, I returned home and found a message on the answering machine from a friend of John's in Holland, asking when John was arriving in London. I discovered that John had been in hospital for ten days in Singapore with double pneumonia and had nearly died; he had been advised to return to London as soon as he was fit to travel. I eventually tracked him down and agreed to meet him in London. I felt elated at the prospect of his return, but was shocked to see how diminished he was, how much weight he had lost, and how fragile he felt. We returned home for breakfast, and John talked of his dying, and what he wanted me to do in the event of his death. Two days later I drove him to the hospital. After two hours of blood tests, X-rays and interviews, as we walked away down the corridor, John announced the verdict he had been given – he was now categorised as having full-blown AIDS. We drove home in sombre mood. I had a thousand questions I wanted to ask and a flood of feelings I wanted to express to him, but I restrained myself and respected his silence. I longed to hug and hold him to reassure him wordlessly by gentle touch, but John was not to be touched.

The weeks following were a roller-coaster of experiences. Without our really having negotiated it, I created a space for John in the house in which he slowly and reluctantly began to make himself at home. For the first time in my life I was sharing my house with somebody whom I loved deeply. At the same time, I was living with someone who was unable to make himself available to me emotionally or physically, and who was coming to terms with living with AIDS. John daily experienced new symptoms and feelings: depression, fear, anger, pain. John steadily withdrew into himself emotionally. There were times when I felt close to despair at the gulf between us and wanted to walk out, or kick him out.

We survived until July, when John moved into his own flat. For three weeks, communication of sorts was restored between us, while I helped him move, but then he withdrew. I sent him cards occasionally. After four months' fantasising about his health and feelings towards me, I decided to visit him. At the third attempt, I met John being wheeled out from his flat on the way to hospital. He had lost the use of his legs and looked a shadow of his former handsome, athletic, muscular self. I asked if he would like me to call at a more convenient time. 'I think not' was his considered reply. It was the last time we met. He died less than a month later, and I attended his funeral as one face among many unrecognised faces – friends from different parts of John's life who met for the first and last time at his funeral, divided in life and unreachable in death.

My capacity for emotional growth and my ability to take the risk of exploring the possibility of friendship with John were both encouraged by my friendship with Richie McMullen. Richie and I had met eight years earlier at the flat of a mutual friend. I found in Richie someone who was able to understand the scars of sexual abuse which I had carried from childhood. At that time, he was involved in his own counselling training and in responding to his own experience of sexual abuse. He put me in touch with a number of people with whom I was able, for the first time, to talk about my own, abused inner child, and about the wounded adult who could so easily be an abuser himself. It was a critical period in my life when the compulsion to act out the needs and distress of my abused child was becoming very strong. Richie, and the contacts I made through him, helped me to recognise the reality of my own abuse and to strengthen the rather weak adult within who was capable, with encouragement, of beginning to look after my child and my deeper need for healing.

Richie was able to identify with many of the experiences I had lived through as child and adult and as a result he was able to understand my motivation at a deep level and be ruthlessly critical. When he felt it was appropriate, Richie could leave aside his non-directive counselling approach with ease. In a series of encounters one August he sat me down and almost bullied me into a state of shock, when I was tempted to let my unhealthy child loose. He pushed and pushed me to enter therapy, but it was only when another emotional crisis occurred that I faced up to the mess I was in and made the crucial move to rescue myself. That was Richie's first gift to me, a bout of ruthlessly directive, confrontational counselling.

His second gift came a few months later. He had moved into a new flat and became ill for the first time, living incommunicado for three months. Later, I realised that this was the first visible effect of his HIV status. He recovered and we met again. I was bored, depressed and unhappy. 'If only . . .' I mused. 'If only what?' Richie encouraged me to dream my unspoken dream. As I unfolded the dreams that I felt I could never realise, Richie said, 'What you're describing is a trip round the world'. And it was. That's what I wanted to do! But I couldn't do that. I couldn't take the time off, couldn't afford it, couldn't leave my responsibilities, couldn't. . . . 'Why not?' Yes, why not? If that is what I really want to do, then why not?

And so I began to put the dream into action. I began to save, something I'd never done before. In 18 months I saved £3,000. I requested an interview with my boss and asked for an early sabbatical. Initially he was unconvinced, but eventually gave my dream his total blessing. Less than a year and a half later I flew off for three and a half months visiting Thailand, Malaysia, Singapore, Java, Bali, Australia, New Zealand and concluding with a rail journey from coast to coast across the States. I took my pain with me, and it returned with me to London. But bit by bit, through the therapy and the sabbatical, my life has changed, and now I am training as a psychotherapist myself.

Richie developed AIDS, went to ground again and we lost touch. It was only in the last week of his life that I was eventually able to thank him for such wonderful gifts to me. But they are gifts which, like the giver, have contained seeds of life and death. The unconfronted me, lacking the courage to make the therapeutic journey, would never have had the courage to meet John and invite him into friendship. But neither would I have befriended a person who was HIV positive and who died after four brief years of friendship. I never found the friendship easy, and I put that down to John's strongly independent self, fearful of being exposed to the feelings of others and ultimately to his own innermost self. It was never easy to be faithful to my commitment to him to be a friend for ever, whatever might happen in his life. It was too easy, out of pity, to feel that I had to sublimate my own needs and feelings to be a perfect friend. This was unrealistic and unhealthy for both of us, but it took a lot of working through for me to realise that. Having had to be responsible for my mother's emotional needs when I was a child, I found something unhealthily attractive in sacrificing myself in looking after John. Through it all, we both grew in our ability to be more honest and emotionally open with one another. At times I was furious with him, but I came to love him deeply.

Richie's gift to me was ultimately the gift of discovering the depth of my capacity to love. That capacity has been strengthened through my involvement in what was a frequently abusive relationship with John. But, without him, I would never have allowed the pain and love within me to be stretched to such a degree. Neither would I have been forced to recognise that there was a very needy, wounded child within, which had begun to scream for the attention and healing which I am now allowing him to receive.

In the last years of his life, I was only involved with Richie's illness and dying at second hand. I was made aware of his moodiness and the impossible demands which he was making, and remembering this helped a little when I was confronted with John's impossible moods. In other ways Richie and John were very different in their response to death. When well, Richie continued to be creatively and passionately involved with the issues which had motivated the later years of his life, and he engaged in the movement towards death with great awareness and courage. John could never accept that his life journey was moving towards death, even to his dying breath. In his last weeks his life was dominated by fear and a desperate fight against his illness. Richie and John were very different people, but each in his unique way gave me great gifts – the ability to nurture my own child, to love and to cry, to feel anger and pain, and the courage to engage with my life path creatively and positively. I give thanks for their healing presence in my life.

Colin Coward

Reflections

When Fr Bill, on behalf of Richie, asked me to write about the impact HIV had had on me from a personal point of view, it seemed an impossible task. There is so much I could say but cannot in case I break confidentiality and so much I would not say as it is too personal. So what is left in between?

HIV is with us and, one way or another, it affects us all. It is a disease that knows no boundaries of age, race, colour, creed or sexual orientation. All those suffering from this infection – the person who is HIV positive, the family, loved ones and friends – need an enormous amount of supportive compassion. The disease is formidable medically but made worse by fear; hate; abusive telephone calls; loss of jobs, lover and family friends; eviction from home. Compassion demands that we offer them acceptance, support and hope. How we respond will determine whether we increase or decrease their sufferings. HIV can be viewed as a challenge and an opportunity for society. It offers us the opportunity to revalue our lives, to consider the meaning of life, and it challenges our compassion. Are we prepared to follow Christ to be with our brother or sister in pain? Christ calls us to be with those in pain, in fear or confusion. In sharing suffering, we minister to one another, and we *both* gain and grow.

In 1985, the Social Work Resource Centre (University College of Wales, Cardiff) was asked for information about what was then a little-known, dimly understood illness called AIDS. As a result of this, a conference was organised for the caring professions; one of the speakers was to be someone from London who was HIV positive. I arrived early on the morning of the conference and found a young man hidden in a corner crying. Without really thinking I sat beside him, put an arm around him and spoke to him. He turned out to be our speaker from London. He had never spoken publicly of being HIV positive; he was very upset, very frightened and very determined to speak; he would not hear of 'giving up'. That evening, when reflecting on the day and his very moving contribution, I realised that he had given me more than the talk. I had wondered how I would react to someone who was HIV positive; would I be able to offer an honest, caring relationship – what Martin Buber would refer to as an 'I-Thou' relationship or what he would call an 'I-It' relationship – that is, would I be so concerned about myself that I had less energy to offer him? I now know the answer. I was so concerned about him and his obvious distress that I had not thought about myself at all.

HIV infection is the opportunistic disease of society in that it has challenged us in many ways and has given us the opportunity to re-evaluate our own lives. It has highlighted the need, not for new, but for good practice. It has made us rethink many things we simply took for granted. It has made us question our professional practice and our private behaviour. It has brought out the best in many people.

Richie McMullen told me it was the best thing that ever happened to him. From being a rolling stone that certainly gathered no moss, he now had purpose and meaning in existence. This is evidenced in the work he then did caring for others: he helped to found Streetwise Youth with Fr Bill; he worked with rape victims and with Martin Dockerell, co-founder of Survivors; he made a number of videos on HIV and wrote a number of books, the royalties often being given away.

Richie was not the only person who felt that his virus had *given* him life. To give just one more example, a mother said it had given her years with her daughter and a new life; if it had not been for this virus she would have been dead long ago of a drug overdose.

In 1988, the Resource Centre worked with others to establish Simama, an accommodation project for people who were HIV positive and either homeless or living in conditions likely to have an adverse effect on their health.

When we first opened Simama, we were wary of the reactions of local people but our pre-conceived ideas proved to be false. When the residents chose to confide in local professionals or neighbours, they responded well. The headmistress of the local school and local clergymen proved to be towers of strength, while the few friends and neighbours who were told reacted positively, often providing practical help and support – such as baby-sitting when a mother was feeling ill.

I have seen someone known to be violent being very gentle with someone very ill, seeing him bending over the bed with concern clearly written on his face. We were overwhelmed by the response of others when we asked for help. Shortly after the project opened, a mother and daughter were thrown out of their home by relatives just before Christmas, with only the clothes they wore. In desperation, we contacted a Methodist church on that Sunday for clothing, bedding, toys, etc, all desperately needed. When I came home from work on Monday, I could hardly get to my door for the piles of bags outside it. We had clothing, toys, food and household goods in abundance, including Christmas fare, and a Catholic priest supplied a bottle of wine!

The churches (Anglican, Catholic, Methodist and the Religious Society of Friends) and the Cardiff HIV Helpline have responded magnificently when asked for specific help. We also received help, encouragement and financial support from a wide variety of individuals from all backgrounds and walks of life – from church congregations, who offered us their Sunday Communion collections, to Richie himself, who donated to the project the royalties from his video about living with HIV, entitled 'Richie'. Help requested has ranged from money, clothing, food, bedding and furniture to support for individuals, foster care to shopping. One priest looked after someone who was very difficult and abusive, with unfailing good humour; he was able to get him into the bath (a major feat no one else seemed to manage) and, when he refused others entry, he would let Father in. He called the priest the most abusive names to his face but, behind his back, said he was a saint!

Care and concern are not only one way, although at times they are unrealistic! In my experience, people who are HIV positive show far more concern for the safety and wellbeing of others than most HIV-negative people. When visiting people at home, I have been told that I could not drink from cups that had not been bleached. Someone who had fallen and cut their head told me that, until the blood was wiped off the wall and carpet, I could not come near. On one occasion, I was carrying something into a house and cut my hand; the panic in case I was infected was incredible – I was the only one bleeding – and later, when I visited someone really ill in hospital, their only concern was my minor cut hand!

Of course, we all know that HIV infection does not always bring out the best in people. Individuals who are HIV positive can face discrimination, harassment and rejection. I have seen examples of this side of human nature as well. I have known someone sleep with a breadknife under his pillow because of harassment. I have known people to be made homeless when family or other relationships break down due (perhaps in part) to their own medical status. Fear and uncertainty are major problems as are many other things but, despite this, HIV remains 'an opportunistic disease for society'.

The Church, historically, has always been in the forefront of compassionate care for the weak, sick and poor. Today, it is increasingly being called to return to this ministry. The churches in Wales have become increasingly concerned and involved with the problems arising from this infection.

Cytun (the Churches Together in Wales) have run a number of courses in counselling people who are HIV positive and many are supporting people who are seropositive and their families.

I have been given so much help and support, often from unexpected people. I know I have gained so much more than I have given, and I have been challenged to rethink many issues. HIV raises many questions: of sexuality, differing patterns of drug abuse, of mortality and death. It challenges our faith and brings us face-to-face with our own insecurities, our own vulnerability and our own fears. How does the Christian gospel relate to the problems and opportunities facing us? How can we best help those faced with a life-threatening illness co-creatively? How do I live as part of the embodiment of the love of Christ? I have plenty of questions but no answers!

Heather Snidle

How Do I Cope?

In 1987, when London Lighthouse was being established in the parish of which I was vicar I spent a sabbatical year exploring what the Church's response to AIDS/HIV might be. Reading a diary I wrote at that time I was reminded of four days I spent in New York, during which I was entertained by a number of personal friends. I was brought up with a jolt as I realised that every person mentioned in the diary for those days is now dead. None of them was particularly ill at the time, as I recall, and certainly I was not aware that they had been diagnosed HIV positive.

Now, five years on in London, it is a similar story: so many of the people who first worked in the field of HIV and AIDS were themselves directly affected by the virus, and many of them are now dead. This significant contribution made by people living with HIV and AIDS in meeting the challenges of the pandemic is the hope within the crisis and, although so many of them have now died, their contribution to the achievements here in London must never be forgotten. Peter Randall, Phillip Langbridge, Richard Chadwick, Colin Clarke, Dietmar Bolle and Richie McMullen are among the growing list of those whose pioneering work has provided me with an inspiration which enables me to go on using my priestly ministry, my sexuality and my HIV positive diagnosis for this work.

I was asked recently during a broadcast of Thames TV's 'The Time – The Place' from London Lighthouse what my thoughts are when I look to the future. My response was 'God knows'! All of us here are having to face daily our friends getting sick and dying and yet still going for life. I just don't know how we do it, but we do. I think that the community which has been created out of this crisis is one of the miracles we all should celebrate and tell the world about. The only way I survive is being surrounded by these people and holding it all together in some tension. And so it is!

AIDS has changed boundaries for so many of us, especially in the caring professions. Doctors, social workers, counsellors, ministers, each are finding their professional expertise challenged time and again by people living with the virus; for me this has been one of the hardest, yet most liberating, experiences of the last ten years.

My involvement in AIDS ministry emerged from being an Anglican parish priest in Notting Hill, where many of those first affected by the virus lived, and also having been around the gay scene for nearly 20 years. From this mix of professional and personal backgrounds, I emerged into working with people who were both my parishioners and my friends. So it is out of this confusion that a new journey of self-discovery began.

I still remember the sense of loss I experienced when working as a chaplain at San Francisco General Hospital and being exposed for the first time in my life to young, mainly gay, men dying every day and not particularly wanting people like me around. It was there that I learnt, painfully, the reality that it's as much an act of ministry to allow someone to tell you to 'fuck off' as it is to administer Holy Communion. The pastor is probably the only professional without a function upon which a dying person is dependent, so to have someone present who can actually be an agent for anger and frustration may become an empowering act which will assist everyone involved. Of course, it raised a whole lot of other issues for me: how to deal with the feelings of rejection and uselessness which these situations raised; having to learn that I do not have any answers, that, if I am really to be a minister in this crisis, I must stay with reality of the pain and powerlessness as it really is.

The religious packaging which I had sheltered behind for years was being challenged, and I felt as if I had no role and no goods to deliver. It was even harder when talking to doctors and nurses who were sometimes expecting me to take over where they were having to leave off as if, somehow, the spiritual professional could make sense of the physical failure.

These feelings were still with me when I returned to London to spend six months working on Thomas Macauley Ward at St Stephen's Hospital, where I had arranged with Charles Farthing and the nursing staff to spend time working as an auxiliary nurse. It was almost a reversal of my San Francisco experience for, while I did learn a great deal about the practical care of people in hospital with HIV/AIDS, I was almost pushed into a pastoral role and, occasionally, urged to exercise my traditional priestly ministry. I suspect this was very confusing to people who, one minute, would find me emptying their bed-pan and the next acting as a pastoral counsellor.

I learnt from this experience, a number of important lessons which we have tried to incorporate into the life of CARA, a pastoral ministry for those affected by HIV/AIDS. First, that the needs of carers must be addressed and that this is best done informally, through friendship and availability. A number of experiments in therapeutic groups for nurses had been tried and simply not worked; so having someone – albeit in an ambiguous role – who was simply there to be, can act as a catalyst for people to unburden themselves or, perhaps, even just have a laugh and a chat in the odd free moment.

Secondly, the need for a community identity which is supportive of everyone engaged in meeting the challenges around HIV and AIDS, from the senior consultant to the volunteer who cames in once a week to do the evening tea round, is essential. It seems to be the experience of many units concerned with HIV/AIDS that a special spirit of community is created from the struggles of a very diverse

range of people facing AIDS/HIV which, at its best, will
include the medical and nursing staff, people living with
AIDS, families, partners, friends and volunteer carers of all
shapes, sizes and colours. This is sometimes an issue which
breeds envy for people engaged in other care groups. I am
thinking, particularly, of a friend of mine who was so bitter
that the ward for elderly confused patients where she
worked had none of the support systems or resources which
were in place in the HIV unit of the hospital where she
worked. I find myself being very confused about this too
for, as I said earlier, we must celebrate what has been
created within the HIV world, yet we must share it with
the outside world and continue to work for a society in
which anyone in need can, and will, receive quality care,
empowerment and attention, however vulnerable.

Carl E Wennerstrom in *Pastoral Care in the Liberal Churches*
wrote in 1970:

> Metaphorically speaking the first liberal might well have been
> the man who helped carry the cross to the place where he was
> crucified. With a job to be done, he was there. With energy to
> be spent, he had it. And in carrying a heavy cross, he was not
> drawn too close together with Jesus. Once the spot had been
> reached and the outcome was certain he dropped from sight;
> we hear no more of this early liberal in the New Testament.
> Perhaps he was off to the circuit court, hoping against hope to
> get a reversal of the conviction and having the courage to try.
> Or he may have been investigating the future support of Jesus's
> family or the burial arrangements, or he may even have been
> getting up a petition to Rome about Pilate. What he was about
> was no doubt of great potential significance. But at the place
> of crucifixion he was absent once the cross had been delivered.
> For a liberal the optimal social distance.

In 1988, three months after I had burnt my ecclesiastical
boats to found CARA I was diagnosed HIV positive. My
health visitor burst into tears as she told me the news, and
I had to comfort her. My doctor could not handle it
and passed me on to his senior consultant. My best friend

at the time said, 'Don't tell anyone, let alone your mother, it will kill her!' I was running an AIDS awareness training session for volunteers that evening. My desert experience had begun! I could no longer be a minister, a carer; I was now a victim. My liberal social conscience was turned inside out. My choices were overnight restricted, any future return to mainstream parochial life very doubtful.

I was no longer a sympathetic fellow traveller who had some insights into the issues; I was faced with horrific isolation in myself which I had heard of from so many newly diagnosed people and, despite the theory, it felt like a death sentence. It was also very hard to realise that many fellow professionals found my diagnosis difficult to handle too. It was in this period that my survival depended less on fellow carers and more on other people living with the virus. It was the challenge of my lifetime and, without the support of a community of people who had been empowered by facing the challenge of the virus, I believe I would have given up.

It was through being part of the self-help networks which were springing up all around London that I was able to put my life in some kind of order, to reclaim the professional side of my life and realise that it was still of value and that I had every right to work alongside others as a carer – a carer who was looking after myself as well as others. That is still very challenging to me, for so much of my condition-ing is about sacrifice and selflessness. I actually wish I had learnt these lessons long ago but when I was trained for ministry we were not given very much insight into these things.

I now believe that it is crucial for all of us involved in HIV/AIDS work, whether diagnosed or not, to know that the issues raised first and foremost are our own. That the primary spiritual need is for all of us to learn to value and care for ourselves. Boundless loving activity on behalf of others is irrelevant, indeed abusive, if we are really hating ourselves, and highjacking other people's experience of pain in order to make ourselves feel better. I think it is right that victim/sufferer/patient language is rejected by people living with HIV/AIDS, for the reality is that, unless we can face ourselves, our own pain and victimisation, we have no right to seek to care for others. Suffering can be as much of a compulsive trip as heroin! That is why I love our CARA training programmes because they present issues which people with HIV and AIDS can help other people to raise for themselves.

I'm still learning these lessons and notice how, when I am physically or emotionally low, I cannot ask for help, so being part of a community network which is in place whether I am there or not is so important.

In combining the role of HIV professional worker and a person living with HIV, I sometimes feel on the edge of both the Church and the HIV establishment. In such a basic matter as funding for CARA, the 'official' Church views us with suspicion and gives no financial support. I find it hard explaining to the secular world that we do not attract significant funding from the official Church which, despite its well-intentioned synodical statements on people with HIV/AIDS, is still trailing behind in a practical response to the AIDS crisis in the UK. As a priest of the Church of England, I am still constantly torn between owning my faith community's lack of commitment to our cause and affirming the many positive responses from individual Christians and communities to the challenge of AIDS.

As a person living with HIV, with a partner who has lived with AIDS for five years and with a full-time job in an HIV project, I am nevertheless enjoying my life as never before. I create more space for myself than in my previous seventeen years' ministry; I have good holidays, lots of fun and a wonderful garden. My relationship with my partner is the most supportive one of my life, and there are times when, together, we feel we can change the world. Since my partner retired from civil engineering following his AIDS diagnosis, he has become an artist, and his paintings are inspiring me, and many others living with the virus, to explore dimensions in our lives we never dreamt existed.*

I am able to say 'no' to taking too many funerals, to withdraw from too much pastoring of others when I have had enough, and to take a great interest in the wonderful world beyond. I am also excited by the opportunities to share in the global responses to HIV/AIDS which have been emerging, not least from the Fifth International Conference for people with HIV/AIDS which took place in London in 1991. I welcome the moves to create more dialogue between scientific, medical, and social work professionals and people living with the virus which was the intention behind the Eighth International Conference of AIDS meeting in Amsterdam in 1992.

My answer to the question, 'How do you cope?' is rooted in the journey of self-discovery. From the very heart of the AIDS crisis, with all its deep pain and loss, is a community of people learning to care for themselves, to share the pain and the opportunities, to create local community support and to develop a global response. I am filled with hope, and will go on inspired and supported by all those who have died, and those who are living with HIV and AIDS.

David Randall

* Artist Charalambos Sofianos, David Randall's partner, died on 30 April, 1993

Journey of Hope

When Frodo Baggins, the Hobbit in J R R Tolkien's book *The Lord of the Rings*, faced the daunting journey to take the Ring to the Cracks of Doom, he exclaimed, 'I am not made for perilous quests. I wish I had never seen the Ring! Why did it come to me? Why was I chosen?' Similarly, I wish I had never seen AIDS – who doesn't? – yet somehow I have been 'chosen' to engage in this journey of joy, sorrow and hope and, like many other people, do so with deep conviction.

My journey commenced in 1985 when a telephone call from a mother within The Salvation Army resulted in my visiting her son in Charing Cross Hospital, caring for him there and at home and, eventually, conducting his funeral, mourning myself for this person who, in so brief a period, had accepted me as a close friend and had made such an impact on my life. Subsequent experience makes me wish I had been more expressive of affection and emotion but, then, we were pioneering, feeling our way on this journey of discovery.

In 1985 in London the gay community in particular was affected by AIDS and, at a time when some prophets of doom were peddling the 'God's wrath' blasphemy and it was erroneously reported as a 'gay plague', there was understandable suspicion of The Salvation Army and its attitude to people with AIDS. The Army had officially adopted the policy of non-judgemental practical and pastoral care and I wanted to make this clear. I determined, therefore: to maintain my uniform-wearing so that people would know where I came from; to make visible the Army's presence among people with AIDS; and to help pave the way for other colleagues to become involved.

Initially, elements within the gay community criticised Mildmay Mission Hospital for planning to care for people with AIDS but, thankfully, the hospital has more than justified its existence and the gay community is very supportive of the work. When in 1987, the Army published the book *AIDS Care: Practical & Pastoral Guidelines* – one of the first such books issued by a Christian denomination in Britain – I was anxious lest the same kind of initial criticism from some people in the gay community have a negative effect. To counter this, and rather than send the book by post, I went to see the editor and staff of *Capital Gay*, feeling like Daniel in the lions' den. But I need not have feared, as I was received with kindness and courtesy and, having explained the Army's official stance and the purpose of the book, I departed, putting my trust in editorial independence. I was thankful for what resulted.

AIDS work by me and other personnel evolved to such an extent that the need for a full-time post at national level was recognised by the Army, and I was appointed as Director of AIDS Support Service. Articles in the Army's press; the development of Oasis AIDS Care Centres in Wandsworth, Chalk Farm, Cardiff, Manchester, etc; lectures and seminars; involvement of individuals in programmes such as AIDS Care Education and Training (ACET) co-operation with statutory and voluntary agencies; the demands of office work – all this and more can be viewed with satisfaction. But involvement with individuals, keeping my feet on the ground, is crucial to my personal experience and always has been high in my priorities as a Salvation Army officer, irrespective of AIDS.

Faith has been confirmed and stimulated, the accretions of the years seen for what they are, and the realities of life, death and life to come brought forcefully to the fore. AIDS has been the common thread drawing us together, but the uniqueness of each individual, known and loved of God, has enriched my experience. The initiative to talk of the spiritual dimension of life has invariably been taken by those with whom I am involved, not least when, bravely, they plan their funeral services, sometimes months in advance, so that it becomes their testimony to life.

Joe* had few close friends, so on many occasions, when in Westminster Hospital or London Lighthouse, I became the recipient of his all-embracing hug. Had it not been for AIDS, I might never have met him and I wonder whether, in normal circumstances, we would have clicked, so to speak, as we did. I had a crucial role to play in his life, not there to render pastoral and practical care alone but also to be a close friend.

Daniel was highly skilled and good-looking but had reared anger like a wall around him to protect his vulner-ability, venting his anger on his few close friends, his fine woman buddy and the nursing staff, but, thankfully, he permitted me to be with him. It concerned me that he was concluding his life in an angry state of mind, yet I was conscious that for me the most important thing was just being there as a fellow human being, he in his blindness and unable to speak, constantly assured of my love and support. Una looked in on us and I took advantage of the fact that Daniel had on a previous occasion permitted her to say the Lord's Prayer with him; holding his hand and that of Una, I said that same prayer again. A few hours remained and I knew that somehow, working within his understanding, I had to give him permission to loose his tenuous hold on life. 'Daniel', I said, 'if you perceive within your heart and mind a light to which you should respond or a door through which you should go, go for it, and God bless you, my love.' And with that, he died peacefully. He had asked to be remembered and I do so with much affection, commending him to the mercy of God. Daniel's yucca plant in my home is a daily reminder of him.

One of the best ways for medical staff to get to know you is when they see you at dawn, having cared for a

* Names of patients have been changed

friend and stayed nights on the ward, looking bleary-eyed and unshaven, attempting to get one's act together before facing another day's demands.

One Sunday I was conducting the services at The Salvation Army Chalk Farm Corps and when I returned to the hospital to be with David during the afternoon, I was urged by staff to remain with him as they expected him to live for just a few more hours and felt that it was important for me to be with him. So my well-intentioned vigil continued. I felt bad at landing someone at the last minute with the task of conducting the evening service. I was all the more embarrassed, however, by the fact that David survived for another three weeks! For most of those weeks, I stayed nights in his hospital room, taking it in turns with other friends to sit with him or doze on a mattress on the floor alongside his bed. It is said that the sense of hearing is the last thing to leave a person but I have a shrewd idea that humour is also one of the last things to depart. Some might have thought it terribly irreverent to hear a group of us in David's room late at night roaring with laughter and indulging ourselves in Big Macs! I believe it was David's sense of humour which prompted him to depart this life during the very weekend when two of us closest to him were on separate engagements in Wales – me receiving word just as I was about to lead a day's conference on AIDS! The façade I presented belied the fact that I was crying within. I gave expression to those emotions at a later time.

Having little privacy in my life, I value all the more my flat in Camberwell. When I close the door, there is an oasis within where, if need arises, I can on bended knee let the tears flow, nature's own therapy, bringing the gift of sorrow to the Lord described as 'a man of sorrows and acquainted with grief'. I am thankful, too, for close friends, especially Michael and George, who bear with me as I wrestle with the inevitable ups and downs of life, or use them as sounding boards for my thinking on issues being faced.

To escape, occasionally, to my home town of Cheltenham to do some gardening for relaxation or to wander over Leckhampton Hill, brings its own therapeutic, if tiring, relaxation. Then, to go to the crowded morning worship at The Salvation Army, sitting quietly at the rear of the premises and to 'drink in' before returning to London in the afternoon, brings spiritual refreshment. Life is more than AIDS and, being always on call, I find it is good to get away from it all and put things in their rightful perspective.

The number of visits I am requested to make to people in home and hospital increases as friends of those with whom I am involved ask if they, too, can be visited; or hospital staff ask me to visit with the agreement of a patient; or someone at a funeral asks if I would visit them or a friend. I find myself often going beyond the role of pastor and carer to that of close friend. Even the date of the necessary annual holiday is influenced by the needs of such friends. Names crossed out of the address book is a reminder that many of us are experiencing multiple losses, far more than is normally experienced in life, at least in this country.

One of the greatest stress factors is that one is involved with predominantly young men and women. In the normal course of life it is the younger generation which grieves the demise of the older, but in AIDS work the roles are often reversed and one finds the need to minister to parents in the loss of son or daughter. As friend and executor for John, I was thankful to be with him in hospital that morning and then, with permission, to go to the station to meet his mother who had travelled from the far north. Bringing her to the ward, we were met with the news that John had just died. Had he intended it so, I wondered? Bearing my own sense of grief, I felt I was on holy ground as I took his mother to see John and prayed with them both. As both mourner and minister, some few days later, I conducted the funeral and then bade farewell to John's mother, clutching in her hands a spray of flowers generously given by the florist.

On another occasion, I was on my way to the ward with the friend of a patient and, passing the hospital chapel, the young man asked, 'Trevor, can we go in for prayer?' There, as we clasped each other's hands, I falteringly prayed for God's blessing, remembering especially the friend with whom he had lived for ten years and who was now concluding his life. Neither of them would claim to be particularly religious yet somehow both young men knew that within the heart of death is the source of life and resurrection comes anew. Life's journey is sustained by that hope.

Trevor A Smith

Getting Acquainted With Death

Now that my mother's older, she speaks louder and I couldn't help hearing her on the telephone. An elderly admirer of hers had died and his son was breaking it gently to her. 'Oh, he died on Monday', boomed my mother in deep distress, 'And the funeral's on Friday'. She paused and then said briskly, 'Now, what's news?' How that son's jaw must have dropped! Later on I explained to him that my mother wasn't being evasive; her Father in heaven has the same warm indulgent love for her as her Yiddish father and mother on earth. So, like many Jews, she dislikes death but doesn't fear it and has no time for hell, even for her enemies. I have inherited her matter-of-factness.

A lady complimented me on my pastry. 'You can't beat marble for rolling it out', I said enthusiastically, 'Cadge a bit of tombstone from the stonemason!' Well, she had another cuppa but no more cake.

Now, I don't want to put you off your food too, but death is the one certainty for us all, so it's prudent to get acquainted. Why not sign up for a contemplative retreat where the retreatants try to die to the world? It's refreshing and most retreat centres have decent beds now – even central heating. You could also help out in a hospice. There's sadness there but mixed with too much love and laughter for tragedy.

Now, I'm not trying to glamorise death. I dislike pain and all functions of the body are messy, whether it's birth, death, making love or masticating food. But a foretaste of your own mortality brings a lot of benefits. It makes you appreciate the present, stops you hoarding, and helps you work out what's worthwhile and what's silly in your life, which is very practical.

Last week, for example, I had to demonstrate some live TV cooking – nothing is more fraught because while you fry and chop, you also smile and chat. Before I even got to the studio, I was in a foul temper. At the hotel, I found I'd forgotten my clean shirt. Breakfast arrived just as I'd soaped myself in the shower and I was caught on the hop; I'd dropped my toothpaste in the loo. When I got to the studio I lost my cookbook and I promptly wished I was dead. Suddenly, I saw my shirt and my lost toothpaste bathed in the light of eternity and I rolled about with laughter. I even hugged a surprised producer, who took it rather well, considering.

Now if you too lose your sense of proportion and, what with the rain and the recession, I don't blame you, here's a spiritual exercise to get it back. Write your own obituary! No, I'm not kinky, and I don't think I'm suffering from any dreadful disease, nor am I trying to depress you. I just want to tell you that death is also a gift of God and, if you make friends with it, it can teach you a lot about life.

Lionel Blue
From *Tales of Body and Soul*, Hodder & Stoughton
© Lionel Blue, 1994

What Will I Do?

What will I do
  when you're not here?
How will I cope
  without your care?
You've taught me so much
  through your fight for life.
You've fought with dignity,
  honesty and might.
AIDS is the disease
  that's taking you away.
It doesn't care
  at what time of day.
It doesn't care how
  you've lived your life.
It doesn't care how
  you've fought the fight.

What will I do
  when you're not here?
You're the one
  who's always cared
Who will I phone
  when I feel down?
The questions keep going
  round and round.
Then I think
  how lucky I've been
to share your life,
  your hopes, your dreams.
I've got your love
  and my memories too.

Cry Love, Cry Hope

You'll always be there
when I need you.

Kath

Processing Together Towards 'The Event'

Tuesday 12 November 1991

Dearest Richie is beginning the last part of his journey in this life. Today, we were able to talk about his dying and what he wants to happen between now and then. I can see the light in his eyes going out – his physical exhaustion, inability to eat, his kidney problems – all confirming what we have both known for the last six months, but have feared acknowledging to each, fear of the pain that is of love, a love that must come from within the dignity of love. We talked of the special gifts he wishes to leave members of his family; of his concern for Stephen and how he will cope; of his concern for who will support me. His courage is there, strong enough to face whatever. It is devastating even though I've been aware that for the past year his quality of life, his being able to enjoy life fully, is diminishing.

I ache as my tears of love, of vulnerability flow and I pray for strength to be alongside him as he wishes, for the strength to allow him to be in full control for as long as possible as he talks of me travelling for two or three months after his dying. There are no words to express how I feel; only my feelings are my words and these I must allow the freedom to heal, to embrace both Richie and myself. We are born alone, we live in our aloneness and we die alone, in the uniqueness of our own dying. Richie must have the space, the love he needs to be involved in his dying. In his dying is also my dying. He has helped me to grow in so many ways. I simply pray that I can assist him as he begins the final lap of his journey which really began about a year ago.

Wednesday 13 November 1991

Today dearest Richie, partner and friend, has gone on to the diamorphine pump to control his pain and also to give him control of his dying. When awake, he is so in control as he always said he wanted to be; what quality of life is there for him now – so frail, so thin, with the light in his eyes growing dimmer? How awful it is to see him in darkness. Yet, on the surface, he shows no humiliation; the pain of his going is mine not his. We cried today with the tears of our loving as we quietly talk about our parting – of the specific gifts he wishes to leave his family, especially his beloved Stephen; his growing love for Nici; the goodness of Kath and Colin, of James and Collet; his sadness over not seeing his nephews or nieces into adulthood. We talk about the wonderful and sometimes painful times shared in our lives as each other's partner. I know the hidden meaning of the pump; how can one really know whether this hastens a life already ebbing away? His brave decision not to return home confirmed when he gave his Stephen the keys, 'It's now your home'. He had a welcome visitor today, whose own pain meant he could not recognise that the welcome visit was becoming a non-welcome visit; so many are afraid of the silence because it highlights their own pain. One forgets so easily the pain we project onto others is ours not theirs. We can only feel our pain and never the pain of others – if only we could and, in some way, ease the other's pain. Dignity of love allows us to be alongside the other person as we embrace each other with our own vulnerabilities, our own sense of utter helplessness.

Thursday 14 November 1991

The funeral today of David – so difficult as though it were a full dress rehearsal for the 'event' of dearest Richie's funeral. The strength came from somewhere as I cried inside – pre-bereavement is painful, especially when you know at gut level your partner is actually, and bravely, moving into the great cloud of unknowing, like the unknowingness of love's journeying into the mystery of the ultimate lover forever remaining a part of one's essential, that which processes into the greater life.

Today we bought a small portable colour television; he wants to keep in touch with the world's activities, with his beloved football, sport, his nature and travel programmes.

Today Peter talks to Richie about ongoing treatment; whether to proceed with active treatment if pneumocystic caninii pneumonia (pcp) should strike again or to let nature take its course. Richie must do what he wishes, and his wishes on this are also mine, whether I will like the decision or not. Realistically, his quality of physical life is not good although mentally he is not depressed. He says, 'I'm learning how to die'. We cuddle and our tears wash each other; they are the tears of love, of pain, always the nourisher of love.

The ward team are being very supportive, not only of Richie and his wishes, but also of me. It is the touch, the embrace that one receives that is of more value than the spoken word for there are no words, only the comfort of silence that understands and accepts the uniqueness of our differing pains and how they are coped with as we make this journey together in our separate ways.

Friday 15 November 1991

I woke up this morning crying and have been doing so nearly all day, except in the presence of Richie, who appears to be bearing up so well. He's told me, during the day, his time for leaving is very close and he wished to see Kath and James. When I asked him how he was feeling about his dying, he said, 'Bill, it will be a great release'. We both agreed we shall miss each other. He is quietly, bravely, and matter-of-factly preparing for his departure and has been thinking a good deal about his mother today.

He's so frail but, thankfully, sound in mind and is alert to everything. I look at him and think, 'Where is his quality of life now?'; his mind rather than his body holds this for him. He was delighted to see Kevin and John, also Maggie and Annie. He tires easily so their visits were good but short.

To be involved in so personal a way is to recognise how vulnerable one is to a deep sense of helplessness and of frustration; there is anger and yet a sense of peace, because Richie is so at peace with all that is going on within himself. The tidiness and security of his room helps, and the nursing team are good, though each one is so different. I find him watching their every move, their style of approach and care. They have different ways of supporting me – some feel they have to say something, others know there is nothing you can say, only honesty helps; they realise there is no point in saying someone is very ill when Richie knows and I know he is dying – a fact is a fact, however painful.

I have spent all day with Richie; a good time of painful sharing of the deep mutuality of our loving, of all the food he has tried to eat, the plain lime jelly he said was absolutely beautiful, so refreshing. At least it stays down but how painful it is to retch when there is nothing to bring up. I'm thankful to be sharing this time with him. We are supporting each other; surely this is what real loving is all about.
Saturday 16 November 1991
Richie, how hard it must be for you – what courage of truth of being fully alive to your dying. How difficult for us both. How wonderful you show us, once again, the richness of the simple, the basic things of life: the sip of ice-cold water, a lime jelly, a portion of peach, a toasted soldier, the comfort of a cigar; the need for tidiness, security, the space to find your own centre anew each day, enabling you to live each minute, each hour according to your desire, insofar as your failing strength allows. What is more, the strength of your peace, your acceptance of your dying, is embracing my pain which is as much for me as for you.

Kath arrived this evening from Cumbria, obviously in much pain from sciatic nerve entrapment. He is so pleased to see her and is now waiting for James's arrival tomorrow. We stay until about 9 pm when he asks us to leave – he had insisted we stayed so late. He had psyched himself up for his family. He so enjoyed Heather, friend and tutor, who helped him so much on his youth and community course twenty years ago and they had a good visit. Heather was responsible for putting Richie in touch with me so many years ago.

Sunday 17 November 1991

Kath and I got to Richie by 11 am. He is pleased to see us. He's had a good night and asks us to sit quietly with him while he centres himself so that he can cope with the day. In a few minutes he then tells us about waking up to find the nurse examining his willie to see if there is any infection around the catheter. He has a Weetabix and says, 'What a wonderful meal'. You would think he had just had a fantastic meal with all the trimmings. The ice-cold water is so beautiful; a hot cloth to his face, a light brushing of his hair, and he's ready for his visitors – his brother James and, later, Gillian, his Hatfield College tutor, who arrives at lunchtime. They have a super period of sharing; they are so fond of each other, James and Stephen (the son he never had). I leave them and Kath to have their special time with him. It's right for each person to have their own space with him.

Today we talk about his dying – he is so supportive of us, as we try to be of him. We want him to be in full control of his dying, his 'event' as he calls it. He says, 'I'm proud of you all, it's wonderful to have my family around'. He asks us to be with him when he dies to this world. Dearest Richie has eaten more today than in any day in past months. He has smoked three cigars; he's been so alive, accepting the conversation and refusing to let us go until his evening medication is beginning to take effect. At 10 pm, he asks us to leave. One of his best days for the past two months – full of sparkle and chat, appreciation and caring for each one. We are amazed at his dignity, his control, his quietness. He is being so gentle with us. We have every desire to go with his wishes and we all, each in our own way, love him deeply. Clearly we are embracing each other with the sympathy of love, courage and truth.

Monday 18 November 1991

Arrived with Kath to see Richie who looks extremely ill, says he's 'buggered'. Richie picked up mentally about 12 noon for Rabbi Lionel Blue's visit. He had a lively conversation on learning how to die; Richie says he gave himself permission to die last Tuesday, 12 November 1991. Lionel gave him a copy of his latest book and reminds us that the next world is in this world, and life is a school for living and dying. James arrives early afternoon. Later in the afternoon, I bathed Richie; his former physical self is being lost, thank goodness his mind remains sharp and gentle. Like Richie, we are learning to centre in to the wholeness of the situation and we are learning how to let go, embraced with our loving. My own feelings are so mixed; they are of sadness, of helplessness and total inadequacy, of being enriched through his dying or as he calls it 'my processing into the event'. 'I'm learning how to let go into total liberation', he says.

Later in the evening there seemed to be a real change in his condition and he was convinced, as I was, that his death was imminent. He says he is dying and wants to be released. 'Dear Bill, my best love. I shall miss you terribly. Take care. Goodbye, my love.' I hold him and let him know it's OK to let go, to process into the great mystery. I decide to stay all night with him as do Stephen, Nici, Kath and James.

Tuesday 19 November 1991.

Long night – couple of hours' sleep in Richie's room. His breathing is so shallow; at times he appears to have ceased breathing.

This morning, about 6 am, Richie comes around and asks for Weetabix, weak tea and a cigar. He is fully awake and seems to have gained so much strength; I wonder if there is something more he has to do or say or if he is simply not ready to initiate fully his 'event'. The other possibility is we are holding him back; we are fearful of letting him go. I hope this is not the case; his quality of life appears to be nil.

During the day Richie says he's surprised to see us, coming out with this comment, 'Good God, it's like the "Woody Allen Show". Last night I was convinced I was dying; now what do I do – do I play dead or accept my total embarrassment?' My feelings are very mixed, delighted and confused; Richie's had another high day, except for the odd time he has been mildly doubly incontinent. I am, by default, becoming his nurse, assisting him in maintaining his dignity as a man, not as a child.

Diamorphine is being increased as his pain increases: for the most part he is in no physical pain. I am experiencing the courage that is his as he proceeds to the event. Richie has been drifting in and out of sleep all day – when awake, he is fully so.

I leave Richie about 9.30 pm to go home for my first full night's sleep in a week of uncertainty. Richie and I have always said we needed to be with each other when his entrance into whatever begins to take place. I hope when this does begin to happen, he will know that he is loved and valued for who he is as a person.

Wednesday 20 November 1991

Richie woke very drowsy, really in a semi-conscious state, looking so tired even though he slept through the night. Perhaps his psyche was working overtime. He slept most of the morning. Pam, his niece, visited him today – a good, sensitive visit.

Lionel Blue also visited Richie and they had a private visit for about two hours. Richie told us later it was very helpful; it was all around his dying. Richie said he has made arrangements, through Lionel Blue, to pay for an African child's education.

During the day, Richie informed Kath and me he is not going towards death; it must come towards him. He also said he had changed his mind about euthanasia, now saw it as all too quick; one would lose the spiritualness of dying so essential to a 'good dying into the event'.

The morphia is consistently being increased, and every time he is moved the pump is used. The bed he is on is terrific, a kind of airbed to prevent sores, etc. Richie has hardly had any fluid intake today and certainly no food. It's as though he has gone beyond the need for food. Most of the day we spent sitting quietly alongside him.

Thursday 21 November 1991

Similar day to Wednesday. Included a short visit from Annie, from Helen and from Steve; Richie spent most of the day sleeping. I sit and watch, taking in his every movement as if to see this for the last time. Similarly, I find myself watching every movement of the nurses and doctors. Today the woman who gives massage came in and massaged Richie. She also tried to draw the pain out of his body by passing her hands over, in a sweeping away from his body from head to feet outwards. But this is not the right atmosphere; one simply cannot walk in and attempt this kind of work without preparation of the others in the room.

Richie has slept most of the day. I went out locally to lunch with Fiona. I could not eat; I only wanted to, and did, cry, hopefully without embarrassing her. Such a lovely person!

Friday 22 November 1991

No real change in Richie today. He is flowing in and out of consciousness; although he has little or no strength, he insists on doing things for himself. It may take five minutes for him to put a spoon to his mouth; he refuses help. I am having to learn to let him continue to help himself however long it takes to make the differing movements, movements we, normally, never think about.

Trying to do things for him lessens his dignity as a person. We help only by keeping away our own feelings of helplessness, our own need to be doing something. When Richie is ready he will ask for assistance to be offered in the way he feels this should be done. Outside-the-family visits he now finds too tiring. He needs us, as we him, to be there in the peace of silence that is so essential during this period in one's life.

Saturday 23 November 1991

No real change except Richie is weaker. His extremities are cold, as those parts of his body are closing. Again he spends the day being in and out of a deep sleep.

During the day there was a phone call from Martin Dockerell to let Richie know that the BBC film on male rape in which he took part has just been awarded the Howard League Media Award and also that a Member of Parliament is placing a Private Member's Bill before the House equalising the law with regard to male and female rape. Richie so thrilled – he clenched his fists and said, 'Thank God'.

Shortly after this news he again moved into a very deep sleep, a semi-conscious state, so much so we thought he might be letting go.

Sunday 24 November 1991

Again Richie surprises us all with waking and asking for the Sunday papers – especially the *Sunday Express* which he would never have in the house. On one level this is great; on the emotional level difficult to handle. How many times does one say 'Goodbye'? How many times must the tears flow? How much emotional pain can I bear?

Richie reads the papers, smokes several cigars during the day and, eventually, says he's tired and wants to sleep the 'deep sleep'. During the late afternoon he lapses into unconsciousness, and I wonder will he really enter into that deep sleep. By the end of the evening, we now feel he is moving along the journey towards what he consistently called 'my event'. Richie could never talk about dying; he disliked the word. It may also have been because as his 'event' drew nearer, he had a sense of continuity.

We stay the night and I hope he will be released into whatever is his future. I hope it is rich in love and a continuing growth. We can only guess. I suppose I guess what I *hope* it will be for him. He has given so much!

Monday 25 November 1991

Richie is, no doubt, making the final part of his journey. His morphine is being increased slightly and we know the effect is accumulative. I wonder if this is what he planned for, what we both label self-selected death. He wants to die – he talked of meeting his mother during the past two weeks. He says he has no fear of death, that he has died many times in his life.

I have great difficulty sitting there all day long watching every intake of breath, the rhythm of his breathing. I can only guess the activity of death within his body, as he lets go in the faith of 'his event', the mystery that has many labels. A man of spirituality such as Richie's could not cope with the institutionalised name for the mystery, so often labelled God, Father, etc. I sit there thinking of the times we shared during our twenty years of a partnership that certainly had its ups and downs. There is no doubt in my mind that he enriched my life and I hope he can say the same of me. He seems so close to moving on that I almost feel I want to help him along – perhaps I'm being selfish in this – while at the same time it's all very sad that his life is drawing to a close.

Tuesday 26 November 1991

Richie is now certainly moving towards 'his event'. All we, all I, can do is to wait. This is not easy; the emotional conflicts are so contradictory. Kath, James, Stephen and I wait with him, as we try to keep ourselves busy, making cups of tea, going for short walks; James and Stephen or Kath and I take turns.

There seems to be a need to increase the morphia and the doctor and nurses refer to me for any change in medication; Richie has told them, 'I trust Bill with my life'. What a trust, what a responsibility, and his family agree.

I am seen, and treated, as the partner – the significant other. This is good; we are able to support each other in truth. There is no doubt Richie is weaker. We spend the time doing basic nursing care as we offer each, in our own way, tender loving care.

Wednesday 27 November 1991

Richie continues his journey while Kath and I stay the night. We had three or four hours' sleep each. We made sure he was never left alone; he wants his family with him when he finally draws his last breath. I wonder when that will be – who knows? For he has a very strong heart we are told. This is no surprise to me. Until 1987, he had a fairly physical life before the great bouts of fatigue started to harass him. He found these became absolutely unbearable. I felt so helpless. It seems to me that, in times like this, all one can do is recognise the mutuality of our helplessness and let it do what it is meant to do. There should be no editing of the emotions.

All four of us spend the day with Richie. His extremities are becoming cold to touch and we want to pile on the blankets. It is difficult to be still with the stillness of the activity of dying. I find myself being unable to eat and almost imprisoning myself at his bedside; this in fear of not being there when he does expire and thus breaking my promise to walk all the way with him.

I went to lunch with one of the nurses in a local restaurant and broke down by a simple comment made – whether deliberate or not, I do not know, but it helped. I have always had difficulty in expressing my emotions; Richie knew how to help me release the pain of being alongside so many who have made the journey he is making.

I give him another shave today. He always looked better to me without a beard. His skin is so smooth and soft. Today the nurse and I bathe him again as we have done almost daily. He was always so thankful that I could help. Touching in this way helped us both and made me feel of some use.

Kath and I decide to stay the night. I believe he is moving ever closer on his journey.

Thursday 28 November 1991

No sleep last night. I feel Richie is now very close to the end of his journey, one that is taking him out of his pain, one that assures me he is moving into his wholeness potential. Another day of watching, waiting and becoming very weary through lack of sleep. Yet it is a time of wonder for me. The experience is so different from that with all the others who have allowed me into their space of dying. This must be because of our closeness that is also our separateness. I feel a part of myself is dying with Richie even though I know there is much of him that will remain – something that can only be offered through what I call the 'friendships of love'. It is the awareness that his physical presence will not be around for me and also others. I suppose I am crying as much for myself as for Richie; I cry that his life no longer has meaning for him, yet I know, intellectually, his reality of life became non-existent; this was only softened, or rather made more bearable, because he was being cared for by the team at the Lighthouse, his immediate family and myself.

Today I'm thinking of the first time I met Richie in May of 1972 when he came down from Liverpool. There was an instant chemical reaction – we just knew we would become friends, partners. In many ways we were so opposite, perhaps this is what created the relationship. We were different enough to complement each other. We both had a great need to care for young people, to release them into becoming themselves. We did this through our respective woundings as young persons – his physical abuse, my psychological and emotional abuse. Through the concern of others for us, our personal abuses became our strengths and the source of awareness of how and what others may have gone through. We believed we were there to encourage understanding, acceptance and growth.

I am alongside him, at his bedside, holding his hand; I sense Richie will finish his journey within the next twenty-four hours.

Friday 29 November 1991

Dearest Richie flowed into the Great Cloud of Unknowing this morning – 3.40 am – into the mystery of (God's) eternal embracing. Richie, thank you for you, for all you gave to me in the mutuality of our loving; no more illness, no more AIDS, only wholeness. Your other half. Much loving Bill.

I prepare Richie, washing him and talking to him all the while, dressing him in clean underwear, T shirt and jeans, his favourite pair of old moccasin slippers.

I embrace him and walk with him to the morgue.

My tears flow.

Saturday 30 November 1991

A day of numbness and a great sense of being lost, of being abandoned. I'm sorry for me. I'm alone; who will look after me? Richie was supposed to do so; this was how we planned it. My whole body aches with the pain of me.

Sunday 1 December 1991

I celebrate the 11 am Mass at St Cuthbert's for Richie, and I cry inside as I do so. Kath comes to Mass with me; James and Stephen are coping in their own way as father and son. The Mass is ended and I feel comforted in some way. I sense Richie shared it with us. The rest of the day is spent sharing our memories of Richie: Kath and James recall their childhoods together; I recall my first introduction to the family in Southport and of Richie wanting to show me the places of his early life in Bootle, where he was an altar boy, and how, like so many Catholic boys, he wanted to be a priest. I shared memories of our trip around England, Scotland and Wales in 1973; our holiday together in M'Sala, Algeria in 1981; our wanderings around London on a Sunday afternoon; our time together at Centrepoint and later at Streetwise Youth. At this time, I was wanting to remember all the good times we shared which certainly outshone the less good times.

We go to a local restaurant to eat even though we do not feel like eating; in fact, we hardly touched the food.

I want to be on my own: I feel this is being selfish; I'm

forgetting what Kath and the others are going through. Kath is here alone and Richie would want me to try to support her. He knew that Stephen and his Dad would support each other. I feel the need to be embraced by a man, so different from the embrace of a woman; it is good to have both kinds of embrace. I guess I'm trying to replace Richie's embrace; of course, this is unrealistic.

Tuesday 3 December 1991

Today we make arrangements for the family from up north to stay in readiness for Richie's 'Event Service' to take place on Friday at the Lighthouse, followed by cremation at Mortlake. I wonder if I will be able to cope, having conducted so many services there in the past years. And what about afterwards? Well, no point in worrying about these matters. I know I will cope until after the service itself. Kath is coping well.

Kath and I go shopping. Kath is looking for something bright and cheerful to wear; of this Richie would approve. He did not want a soberly dressed funeral; he wanted a celebration of colour as his life was colourful.

We do all we can to make sure the service reflects Richie – his concerns, his friends and his caring.

The time seems to be dragging. We have a need to keep busy; the silences force us to think about Richie and of our total inadequacy due to the great sense of loss. None of us likes to let go. I, like so many, want to hang on and this is certainly contradicting what we say we want. And that is Richie's total release; he did not want to be held back by our needs.

A visit to the undertakers again. Richie requested his ashes to be placed in a small casket for eventual burial in the grave of his parents – a total return home for Richie.

Monday 2 December 1991

Not much sleep last night. Now I must begin the formalities, essential for the 'Event Service' to take place at Mortlake Crematorium after the main service at London Lighthouse.

First, to London Lighthouse to get the death certificate and then on to Old Chelsea Town Hall, Kings Road, to the Registry of Births, Marriages and Deaths. Kath comes along with me; I see the registrar alone. He needs other information that is not on the death certificate: was I present at Richie's death? What work did he do? – a youth worker, counsellor, writer, campaigner etc; burial or cremation and where?; how many copies of the certificate are needed? – better get half-a-dozen.

On to the undertakers, who were very sensitive and understanding. Had he paid for his funeral? Was it cremation or burial? Where is it to take place? How many cars? What about flowers? In my confusion, I give the wrong names and addresses. Time seems to have come to a halt. I want the service to be over. At least the business keeps one's emotions at a distance.

Later on with Kath, James and Stephen, we work out how we are to fulfil Richie's wishes as regards his service. The family decide to leave it all to me as Richie and I had discussed the service, both music and words. I was to take the service and offer the eulogy. We decide to have the service sheet printed, to include a picture and to place a notice in the *Independent*.

I spend the evening trying to work out the design and order of service and get it to the printers next day to be ready by Thursday at the latest.

The whole thing is like being in a fog with dim headlights. Hard to believe Richie is dead, yet I know he is. I wonder where he is and what are we talking about when we say 'heaven', or 'the mystery', or 'in the clouds of unknowing'. I think the latter is the most honest fact.

Wednesday 4 December 1991

Another long day. A day of waiting and of some kind of expectation – perhaps the news that Richie is only unconscious, that he will rise again as Lazarus did because of being touched by the profound love of Jesus and the women who loved him. Within, there is a kind of hope that he will live through the long crucifixion of AIDS. Yet, I know, deep within, he is with me and that he has moved into the greater place, situation, whatever the label – if, indeed, there can be such a label for what the mystics call 'the cloud of unknowing'. Strange they do not label the beyond. Perhaps the beyond for Richie is within all he loved and all who loved him. Perhaps he resides or, indeed, has become his 'green parrot'.

It's been a day of holding each other, embracing each other with our differing thoughts and memories of Richie – a man of many contradictions, a constant searcher who questioned so much about religion. His own spirituality would not allow him to get involved in religion per se, especially when structured, institutionalised. He was, indeed, a free thinker attempting to anchor himself in the faith of truth.

As I go to bed this night, I ask him for his support during his 'Event Service' tomorrow. May we all do justice to this event and rejoice that he is now free. Lord, lettest now thy son, Richie, depart and arrive in peace – the peace of love that contains all understanding.

Thursday 5 December 1991

The 'Event Service' took place at 3 pm today, at the London Lighthouse. Just before the service, I placed a beautiful red rose in his hand and kissed his peaceful and cool face. Bon voyage into wherever. We each brought him one yellow rose to go with him to the service and beyond.

Heather, who introduced us some twenty years ago, read, as did Fr Barry who was a volunteer with Centrepoint when Richie and I worked there in the early '70s, and others, including Fr Damian of SSF; Richie, like his mother, always had a soft spot for St Francis, so it was good that Fr Damian could be there to take part.

The service at the Lighthouse went well, even though I broke down while offering the eulogy; the pain of love is more than the emotions of love. About fifty friends and colleagues turned up to share and to support each other.

At 4 pm, we said our 'Au revoir' to dear Richie. For me it can never be a final goodbye. We were, and are, a part of each other's souls.

We returned from the Mortlake crematorium to the Lighthouse and joined those who stayed behind for tea and a time of sharing memories and thoughts.

We returned to Richie's flat for a glass of champagne and sandwiches – turned out to be coffee and sandwiches. The atmosphere was full of the tensions of pain, the pain of loss. We have lost his physical presence but not, I am sure, his spiritual presence. The flat did not feel the same, as though it, too, was mourning the loss of the man who made it such a warm and hospitable place to be in; to rest him; to comfort him during his very long, and at times painful, illness. Yet he grew so much spiritually and, while he was hindered physically, his mind, his creativeness as a writer, grew and we are all the richer for this.

By 6 pm, all members of the family departed towards their own homes. Stephen and James stayed in Richie's, now Stephen's, flat. I returned to my own, took a large whisky to bed and listened to the live production of Mozart's Requiem on television. Seems the right way to close the day in which we, I, celebrated with a kind of joy – the joy of knowing that my dear partner no longer is suffering and dying from AIDS. I know he is safe, in this great 'cloud of unknowing'. He remains very much a part of the fabric of my life, enriched by the dark and lighter threads of his life, unique to no-one else. His physical presence has now become his transfiguration; that is his spiritual presence continuing to enrich and embrace me. All this does not prevent me from crying. Is it for my own self or for Richie? Maybe the tears are honestly for both . . .

Well, my love . . .

To Liverpool and Home

To Liverpool and home, beside his parents, we inter Richie's ashes. I leave London-Euston for Liverpool on the 8.40 am train. How strange it feels to be carrying Richie's mortal remains back to Liverpool, the city of his birth – the place he could not get away from quickly enough. It is the place he left at the age of 16; the place he so proudly showed me around some twenty years ago.

I am met at the station by Kath and Colin, with Ian and Craig, their two sons, and we drive through Bootle where he was born during the Second World War. This trip recalled my first visit with him as, proudly, he showed me the street he played on, the school and the church he attended. We went down to the beach at Waterloo and we drove along the former dock area, so exciting to Richie in his youth and from where he sailed for China and back as a cabin boy at the age of 17. He seemed to want me to soak up his early life at that time; he was not yet ready to share with me the painful area of his youth.

This was a journey rich with reawakened memories of my visits to his family in the early '70s: of sharing with him his mother's dying on a Christmas Eve and of attending her funeral, as I had his father's a few years earlier; of being a guest at his sister Kath's wedding and sharing in the wedding of his brother and the baptism of their young son. On the way to the cemetery, we stopped for lunch even though I did not feel like eating.

We arrived at the Sacred Heart Cemetery, Liverpool Road, Ainsdale, Merseyside at about 1 pm where Jim and Collette were waiting. Together we interred his ashes, as he requested, beside his Mom and Dad. If you like, we buried the chemicals of creation that contained the uniqueness of his soul 'now departed this life.' It was 'ashes to ashes and dust to dust'; it was also, I believe, 'soul to soul'. As we interred his ashes, the thought came to me that our bodies bear the imprint of the beginnings of all creation. I sense that Richie's soul-mind returns to what Teilhard de Chardin referred to as 'the noosphere', what others refer to as 'the psibank', the mystery commonly referred to as 'heaven'.

I cover his wee casket with the earth that has been nurturing his parents' bodies for the past ten years. The soil is so soft to touch, like silk; somehow this is very comforting. Even so, placing the final soil over the casket causes me to well-up and cry with my whole body.

Yet, somehow, I seem to be aware that, deep within myself, the uniqueness of his soul, his loving, has not only rejoined with his parents, but also he is now, more than ever, linked into the uniqueness of the soul of his creator, also my creator, who is, after all, our ultimate lover. I feel that Richie now shares in the mystery where dust and ashes have no dominion and where death has no dominion over love.

After we have interred his ashes, we return to Pam, his niece's, home and with Paul share a meal full of memories. How different are all our memories of Richie and the effect he had on all our lives. I return home by the 5 pm train.

When I eventually arrive home, as if to finalise the day, I read through 'A Celebration of His Life' service and, as I did so, realised it is loving and being loved that gives meaning to, and eternalises, all our lives.

Let the dreams that are gone asleep fast my love,
    Let the tears and fears of yesterday's storm,
For the darkness you saw is past my love,
    So smile a new day is born.
The seasons of life will go on my love,
    And the sails of yours may be torn
But the secrets beneath your feet my love,
    Are the flowers yet to be born.
Let the tears that you shed fall sweet my love,
    For the pain goes and rainbows come without warning
All the seasons will surely return my love
    And a new life will be born in the dawning.

Author unknown
Bill Kirkpatrick

For Bill

LOVE IS . . .
Love is uniqueness
Conformity damned.
Love is completeness,
Individually profound.
Love is straight,
And love is gay,
Love is great,
And love, the way.
Love's a sister,
A nephew and brother.
Love's a vista,
A view of another.
Love is freedom,
Without any chains
Love is free from
Wanting and gains.
Love is a second,
An hour, a day.
Love is a weekend,
A power to stay.
Love's a treasure,
Tremendous wealth.
Love's a measure,
My sense of self.
Love is one,
Or two or three.
Love is gone,
Without the we.
Love is giving
What we can.

For Bill

Love is living,
While we can.
Love's for sharing,
Myself with others.
Love's for caring,
For health in lovers.
Love is Being,
A poet with wings.
Love is Doing,
Simple things.
Love is a child,
Not fully grown.
Love is a wild,
Sea unknown.
Love's the link,
When a loved one dies.
Love's the drink,
From tear filled eyes.
Love is for ever,
It eternally pervades.
Love is moreover,
How to face AIDS.
                         Richie